D1488505

Introduction to

SPECIAL RELATIVITY

Introduction to

SPECIAL RELATIVITY

T. M. Helliwell

Assistant Professor of Physics
Harvey Mudd College

ALLYN AND BACON, INC.

BOSTON

PREFACE

THE PURPOSE OF THIS BOOK is to present special relativity by em-
phasizing the physical content of the theory. Numerous illustrations and
examples are discussed at the early stages, while the concise mathematical description is postponed until after the reader has had an op-
portunity to build up some physical intuition for what is going on. The
plan of the book was fixed partly by experience in trying various orders
of presentation, and partly by the desire to make it useful in a variety
of situations. The core of the book is contained in Chapters III-VI.
Here very little mathematics is used, because very little is needed. It
is the physical ideas and the apparently paradoxical results which are
sometimes difficult.

The first two chapters review some of classical physics and describe
experiments leading up to the special theory. Chapters III-VI culmin-
ate in the Lorentz transformation of Chapter VII. Thus the mathematical outcome of Einstein's postulates is postponed until after time
dilation, length contraction, and the relativity of simultaneity have already been deduced.

Except for Chapter XIII on four-dimensional spacetime, the rest of the
book can be classified as relativistic dynamics. It is designed in such
a way that one can stop after any chapter without a sense of hanging in
the middle, so the material covered can be easily adjusted to the time
available. Chapter XI takes up many examples of collisions and decays
of elementary particles, since this is one of the most important modern
applications of relativistic energy and momentum. Relativistic force,
less fundamental than energy or momentum, has been relegated to the
last chapter. The many appendices are partly for fun and partly for
more advanced topics. Many of them are referred to in the book as interesting sidelights or as giving more detailed explanations.

The author would like to thank many students and faculty members of Harvey Mudd College for helpful comments, and he is especially grateful to Professor Enos Wicher for several valuable criticisms. Also he is indebted to Mrs. Evelyn Lee for an expert and patient typing of the manuscript.

T. M. Helliwell

TABLE OF CONTENTS

Introduction to

SPECIAL RELATIVITY

CHAPTER I
INERTIAL REFERENCE FRAMES AND CLASSICAL MECHANICS

THE SPECIAL THEORY OF RELATIVITY is a theory about space and time. It is not primarily about mechanics, electricity, elementary particles, or any other particular "branch" of physics. But since space and time are the arena in which physical events take place, it is reasonable that a change in our ideas about them might have repercussions throughout physics. That is what has happened. Though revolutionary, relativity grew out of what had gone before — in particular, it developed from the confrontation of Newtonian mechanics with the theories of light and electromagnetism of the nineteenth century. We'll begin in this chapter by briefly reviewing some of the ideas of classical mechanics.

The theory of motion finally presented by Isaac Newton in his Principia was very slow in developing — the concept of inertia and the connection between acceleration and "force" were not easily established. Newton's first law of motion, often called the law of inertia, states that a body will neither change its speed nor its direction of motion unless a force is exerted upon it. A very great deal is implied by this statement. In order to verify it, we must previously have chosen a frame of reference from which our measurements are to be made, and have equipped ourselves with apparatus like meter-sticks and clocks for making measurements. We then contrive to remove all forces from some object, and see whether or not it moves in a straight line, covering equal distances in equal time intervals. Now even if our meter-sticks and clocks are very accurate, and we have managed to remove all forces acting on the object, it is likely that our measurements will conflict with the law of inertia. For example, if the frame of reference we have chosen is fixed to ourselves as we bounce on a trampoline, the object will not move at constant velocity from our point of view. Even if our coordinates are fixed to the surface of the earth, it is known that the first law doesn't hold.

1

The law of inertia is therefore not true if tested by arbitrary observers. But it was Newton's belief that there <u>are</u> frames of reference such that if observers make measurements while standing in one of these frames, they will find the law to be true. A frame with this property is said to be an <u>inertial frame of reference</u>. So the first law is not so much a "law" as a means of <u>defining</u> inertial frames. In principle, in order to see whether or not we are standing in an inertial frame, we can watch the motion of an unforced object. If it starts at rest and remains at rest, or if it continues to move with its initial velocity in the same direction, we would pronounce ourselves inertial observers, at rest in an inertial frame of reference. The importance of the first law is that it singles out a special kind of reference frame, the inertial frame, as particularly simple and significant.

Newton's <u>second</u> law states that the acceleration of an object and the net force exerted on it are related through the object's mass by the equation $\vec{F} = m\,\vec{a}$. Again, this law is clearly not true if applied by an arbitrary observer, since someone bouncing on a trampoline will see things accelerate without any forces to account for it. But it is just as clear that it is again <u>inertial observers</u> who are favored above all others. It is they, and <u>only</u> they, who can use Newton's second law! For if no unbalanced forces act on an object, the second law claims that it won't accelerate, so must move in a straight line at constant speed. This is nothing more than the condition defining inertial observers, which came from the first law. So the second law cannot be correct for an accelerating observer, because it predicts constant-velocity motion if there are no forces. In short, the first law should not be thought of as a special case of the second law, for situations without forces, but rather as a means of specifying those observers for whom the second law is valid.

According to Newton, then, there are an infinite number of reference frames from which the world can be studied with the aid of the second law — namely, all those frames moving at constant velocity. An observer or a group of observers in a given frame can construct for themselves a set of coordinate axes by which the position of any object can be labeled, and can also have clocks in order to tell when things happen.

To cover four measurements with one word, it is convenient to define an event as something which happens at a point in space and an instant in time. Thus if two particles collide at position x = 2, y = 3, and z = 1 meter, and at time t = 5 seconds, the event can be characterized by the four numbers (2, 3, 1, 5).

Obviously the measurement of the position of a given event will depend on the observer's frame of reference. Suppose, for example, we consider two inertial frames moving at relative velocity V along their mutual x-axes, as shown in Figure 1.1. By convention we will specify that the primed frame S' is moving to the right with respect to the unprimed frame S. Thus, if some event occurs in space and time, people in S will label it by (x, y, z, t), whereas people in S' will label it (x', y', z', t').

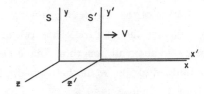

Figure 1.1

The two sets of numbers must be related to each other, and it would seem from common sense that if the same standards of length and time are used in both systems, and if all the clocks are synchronized and set to t = t' = 0 just as the origins of S and S' coincide, the relationships must be

$$x' = x - Vt$$
$$y' = y$$
$$z' = z \tag{1-1}$$
$$t' = t$$

for any given event. These relations, which are collectively called the "Galilean transformation," simply state that an event measured in the S-frame (with coordinates x, y, z, t) will be at exactly the same place and time in the S'-frame, except for the x-coordinate, which is corrected for the fact that the origin of the S'-frame has moved away from the origin of the S-frame by a distance Vt. It is possible for an event to be at positive x, and negative x', which will happen if the origin of the S'-frame has moved past the position of the event before it happens.

Notice, from the Galilean transformation, that lengths and time intervals are the same in the two frames. If x_1 and x_2 are the x-coordinates of the

3

two ends of a meter-stick at rest along the x-axis of the S-frame, the length of the stick will be $x_2 - x_1$. In the S' frame the meter-stick is moving, but its length as measured by S' observers will be $x_2' - x_1'$, which is $(x_2 - Vt) - (x_1 - Vt) = x_2 - x_1$, or the same length (1 meter) as that measured in the unprimed frame. In other words, primed observers can address their unprimed friends: "You claim your meter-stick is one meter long, and we have found that it is one meter long from our point-of-view, also." Note that <u>two</u> measurements are required (x_1' and x_2') which we've assumed are made at the <u>same</u> time. The assumption that the measurements are made simultaneously is really part of our definition of the length of a moving object — we would certainly not want to measure the position of the two ends at different times. In order to make an accurate length measurement, at least two observers with synchronized clocks would be needed. If the front of the stick passes by one observer just as the back passes by the other, then the distance between them is the length of the stick.

If the meter-stick were tilted with respect to the x-axis, its length would still be the same in every inertial frame of reference, as can easily be shown from the full set of transformations for x, y, and z. Similarly, a time interval $t_2 - t_1$, measured by observers in the S-frame, is the same time interval measured by observers in the S' frame, since $t_2' - t_1' = t_2 - t_1$. How could this be verified experimentally? Suppose a clock is at rest in the unprimed frame, and we are at rest in the primed frame. Since we want to read the clock at two different times, we will again need two observers with synchronized clocks. As the unprimed clock passes one observer, he will note both the reading of the unprimed clock (t_1) and also the reading of his own clock (t_1'). Some time later, the unprimed clock passes by the other observer, who notices that it reads time t_2, whereas his own clock reads t_2'. The observers can then compare notes, and if the Galilean transformation is correct, they will find that $t_2' - t_1' = t_2 - t_1$.

According to the Galilean transformation, space and time are entirely distinct notions, which never become confused, and which have no influence on the behavior of material bodies. People searched for laws

4

governing the motion of objects in space and in time, without really investigating space and time themselves. According to Newton, "absolute space, in its own nature and without regard to anything external, always remains similar and immovable." Also, he said "absolute, true, and mathematical time, of itself, and by its own nature, flows uniformly on, without regard to anything external." [*]

The Galilean transformation says more than just how to find x', y', z', and t' in terms of x, y, z, and t. It also shows how to find the velocity of a particular particle in one frame in terms of its velocity in a different frame. We have used the symbol V for the relative velocity of the two frames S and S', so we will call the particle velocity $\vec{v}$ in the S-frame and $\vec{v'}$ in the S'-frame. By definition of velocity, $v_x = \frac{dx}{dt}$, $v_y = \frac{dy}{dt}$, and $v_z = \frac{dz}{dt}$, so the Galilean transformation gives

$$v_x' \equiv \frac{dx'}{dt'} = \frac{d\,(x-Vt)}{dt} = \frac{dx}{dt} - V \equiv v_x - V$$

$$v_y' \equiv \frac{dy'}{dt'} = \frac{dy}{dt} \equiv v_y \qquad\qquad (1-2)$$

$$v_z' \equiv \frac{dz'}{dt'} = \frac{dz}{dt} \equiv v_z$$

which is exactly what you would expect. v_y and v_z are the same in both frames, but v_x differs by the relative velocity of the two sets of coordinates. For example, a bullet going at 2000 feet/sec will only appear to be going 1500 feet/sec if you are running with it at 500 feet/sec. Here the S-frame is the ground, you are in the S'-frame, v_x is the velocity of the bullet relative to the ground, v_x' is its velocity relative to you, and V is your velocity relative to the ground. This is just the well-known rule of vector addition for velocities.

If another derivative is taken, we obtain the transformation rules for acceleration:

---

[*] See E. Mach, Science of Mechanics, 6th edition, pp. 271 and 276, Open Court Pub. Co., 1960.

$$a_x' \equiv \frac{dv_x'}{dt'} = \frac{d\,(v_x - V)}{dt} = \frac{dv_x}{dt} \equiv a_x \quad (V \text{ is constant})$$

and similarly $a_y' = a_y$ and $a_z' = a_z$.

(1-3)

Thus the acceleration of an object is the same in all inertial frames, according to the Galilean transformation. This is a very interesting result, because if we assume that the mass of a particle is constant, the quantity $m\vec{a}$ in Newton's law is the same in all frames. Therefore if $\vec{F} = m\vec{a}$ is a fundamental law of nature, which can be used equally well by any inertial observer, we must expect that any given force $\vec{F}$ would also be the same in all frames. Experiments up to the end of the nineteenth century had confirmed this expectation. The equation $\vec{F} = m\vec{a}$ is therefore said to be "invariant under the Galilean transformation," meaning only that it is equally good in any inertial frame if the Galilean transformation is used to translate variables from one frame to another. There is no preferred frame of reference. Any inertial observer can use the equation. This requirement of invariance of fundamental laws is very powerful, and we will have more to say about it when we begin discussing relativity in Chapter III.

Newton's <u>third</u> law states that "action equals reaction,"[*] or that if one particle exerts a force $\vec{F}$ on a second particle, the second particle exerts a force $-\vec{F}$ back on the first particle. Thus if a number of particles are considered together as a group, and if no outside forces are applied, there is no net force on the group, due to cancellation of all the internal forces. This fact is important in establishing the significance of <u>momentum</u>. Consider for a particle of mass m and speed $\vec{v}$ the product $\vec{p} = m\vec{v}$. Since the particle's acceleration is defined to be $\vec{a} = \frac{d\vec{v}}{dt}$, Newton's second law can equally well be written $\vec{F} = \frac{d\vec{p}}{dt}$. If no force is exerted, the momentum $\vec{p}$ remains constant in time, or is said to be "conserved." This is a trivial result since it just reproduces the law of inertia.

---

[*] The third law is discussed in more detail in books on classical mechanics, such as those listed at the end of the chapter.

6

But now consider instead a group of particles, and define their total momentum $\vec{P}$ as the vector sum of the momenta of the individual particles. That is, define $\vec{P} = \vec{p}_1 + \vec{p}_2 + \ldots \vec{p}_n$. If we also define a total force $\vec{F}_{Total}$ as the sum of the forces on individual particles, namely $\vec{F}_{Total} = \vec{F}_1 + \vec{F}_2 + \ldots \vec{F}_n$, we can write a grand second law $\vec{F}_{Total} = \frac{d\vec{P}}{dt}$ just by adding up the equations for all particles. If we further split up the total force into the forces exerted by external agents and by members of the group themselves, we can write

$$\vec{F}_{Total} = \vec{F}_{external} \qquad (1-4)$$

since the total internal force is zero, a consequence of Newton's third law. Now the importance of momentum is evident. For if no external forces act on the group (although there may be many internal forces), the total momentum $\vec{P}$ is conserved. Individual particles may move in complicated ways, but they always move in such a way as to keep $\vec{P}$ constant.

Aside from the total momentum $\vec{P}$, another quantity characterizing a group of particles is their center of mass $\vec{R}$. Suppose we stand in a particular frame of reference, and measure the radius-vector $\vec{r}$ from the origin of our coordinate system to each particle in the group. Let the ith particle have mass m_i, and be at position $\vec{r}_i$, as shown in Figure 1.2.

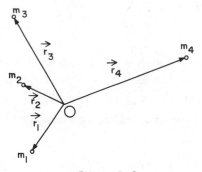

Figure 1.2

Then the center of mass of the group of (say) $\underline{n}$ particles is defined by the vector

$$\vec{R} = \frac{m_1\vec{r}_1 + m_2\vec{r}_2 + \dots m_n\vec{r}_n}{m_1 + m_2 + \dots m_n} = \frac{\displaystyle\sum_{i=1}^{n} m_i\,\vec{r}_i}{\displaystyle\sum_{i=1}^{n} m_i}. \qquad (1\text{-}5)$$

The vector $\vec{R}$ gives the point in space about which all the particles "balance," in the sense that if they were all rigidly connected to the center of mass by weightless rods, and the center of mass were supported against gravity by a pin, the assembly would balance perfectly and not tend to fall over.

The time derivative of the center of mass is

$$\frac{d\vec{R}}{dt} = \frac{d}{dt}\frac{\displaystyle\sum_{i=1}^{n} m_i\,\vec{r}_i}{\displaystyle\sum_{i=1}^{n} m_i} = \frac{\displaystyle\sum_{i=1}^{n} m_i\,\frac{d\vec{r}_i}{dt}}{\displaystyle\sum_{i=1}^{n} m_i}$$

differentiating the sum term by term, and using the fact that the particle masses remain constant. But the velocity of particle $\underline{i}$ is $\vec{v}_i = \dfrac{d\vec{r}_i}{dt}$, and its momentum is $\vec{p}_i = m_i\vec{v}_i$. Therefore

$$\frac{d\vec{R}}{dt} = \frac{\displaystyle\sum_{i=1}^{n} \vec{p}_i}{\displaystyle\sum_{i=1}^{n} m_i} = \frac{\vec{P}}{M} \;, \qquad (1\text{-}6)$$

where $\vec{P}$ is the total momentum of the group of particles, and M is their total mass. Since the derivative $\dfrac{d\vec{R}}{dt}$ is in fact the velocity of the center of mass, we have proven that the center of mass moves at constant velocity whenever $\vec{P}$ is conserved — that is, whenever no external forces are exerted.

If the total momentum of the system is zero in some particular frame of reference, then the center of mass remains fixed in space. This particular frame is called the "center of mass frame," and can be thought of either as that frame in which the center of mass remains at rest, or as that in which there is no total momentum.

8

Another quantity which is conserved in classical mechanics is the total energy of a particle, or group of particles. Suppose that a particle moves under the influence of a force. For simplicity we will take both the motion and the force to be in the x-direction. The work done by the force on the particle in going from x_1 to x_2 is defined to be

$$W = \int_{x_1}^{x_2} F\, dx .$$

$(1-7)$

Now since $F = m\frac{dv}{dt}$, and by the chain rule $\frac{dv}{dt} = \frac{dv}{dx}\frac{dx}{dt} = \frac{dv}{dx} v$, the integral is

$$\int_{x_1}^{x_2} F\, dx = m \int_{x_1}^{x_2} \frac{dv}{dx} v\, dx = m \int_{v_1}^{v_2} dv\, v$$

$$= \frac{1}{2} m v_2^2 - \frac{1}{2} m v_1^2$$

$(1-8)$

where v_1 and v_2 are the particle velocities at positions x_1 and x_2. Defining the kinetic energy to be K. E. $= \frac{1}{2} m v^2$, we've found that the change in kinetic energy equals the work done.

The work $W = \int_{x_1}^{x_2} F\, dx$ done on a particle may or may not depend upon the path taken by the particle in going from x_1 to x_2. In the one-dimensional situation we have been assuming, possible paths are limited, but the particle may start at x_1, back up, return to x_1, and then proceed to x_2. If more work is needed to take the particle this way than directly from x_1 to x_2, the work is path-dependent, and the corresponding force is said to be non-conservative. Frictional forces are non-conservative, since the longer the path taken by a particle in going from one point to another, the more work is done on the particle by the forces of friction. Gravitational forces, on the other hand, are conservative: no more net work is done by taking a long path than a short path.

For <u>conservative</u> forces, the integral $\int_{x_1}^{x_2} F\,dx$ depends only on the end-points x_1 and x_2 (and not upon the path), so we can define a unique number

$$\Delta U = - \int_{x_1}^{x_2} F\,dx$$

which is called the difference in <u>potential</u> <u>energy</u> between the points x_1 and x_2. Potential energies can be defined at each end-point, such that their difference is

$$U_2 - U_1 \equiv \Delta U = - \int_{x_1}^{x_2} F\,dx \;. \tag{1-9}$$

U_2 and U_1 are only defined within an additive constant, since it is only their difference $U_2 - U_1$ which has a physical meaning. Combining (1-8) and (1-9), $\Delta K.\,E. = -\Delta U$, or

$$U_1 + \tfrac{1}{2} m v_1^2 = U_2 + \tfrac{1}{2} m v_2^2 \tag{1-10}$$

saying that the <u>total</u> energy (potential plus kinetic) is always the same, which is to say that it is <u>conserved</u>.

We've restricted ourselves here to one-dimensional motion for simplicity, but it is straightforward to show that energy is also conserved for three-dimensional motion of an arbitrary number of particles, as long as all forces are conservative.

As everyone knows, Newton's laws, the Galilean transformation, and the whole of classical mechanics provide an excellent description of the motion of objects. Scientists and engineers have used them for centuries in a wide variety of situations. But toward the end of the nineteenth century, when the study of light and electromagnetism became sufficiently advanced, difficulties were uncovered. This is the topic of the next chapter.

REFERENCES

1. A more complete discussion of topics in this chapter can be found in books on elementary classical mechanics, such as Physics by Resnick and Halliday (John Wiley & Sons, 1960), Elementary Classical Physics by Weidner and Sells (Allyn & Bacon, 1965) or University Physics by Sears and Zemansky (Addison-Wesley, 1960).

2. A film entitled "Frames of Reference," produced by PSSC-ESI, is available. It is distributed by Modern Talking Picture Service, Inc., 3 East 54 Street, New York 22, New York.

PROBLEMS I

1. A particle has a position $x(t) = v_o t + \frac{1}{2} a t^2$ and velocity $v(t) = v_o + at$ as a function of time, measured in the unprimed frame. Find its position $x'(t')$ and velocity $v'(t')$ measured in a primed frame moving to the right of speed V relative to the unprimed frame, using the Galilean transformation.

2. A 3-1/2 ton two-horned African rhinoceros charges at 30 miles/hour into a 7-ton ball of putty sitting on a frictionless sheet of ice in a perfect vacuum. Assuming the rhino gets stuck in the putty, find the final velocity of the two. Is kinetic energy conserved in the collision?

3. Two identical billiard balls A and B undergo a glancing collision without loss in total kinetic energy (i.e., an elastic collision). Before the collision, their velocities are v_x^A = 10 m/sec, v_x^B = -10 m/sec and no component in any other direction. After the collision, v_x^A = -6 m/sec, and both balls have a y-component of velocity as well as an x-component. Find v_x^B, v_y^A, and v_y^B following the collision. (Assume v_y^A is positive.)

11

CHAPTER II
LIGHT AND THE ETHER

DURING THE NINETEENTH CENTURY, as a means of trying to understand light-waves, it was believed by many physicists that the universe was filled with a substance called "ether." There were at least two excellent reasons to believe in the existence of ether. First of all, it was felt that all waves require something to "wave" in; water waves need water, sound needs air, etc. Light then must wave in "ether," because something is needed to provide the restoring force necessary to maintain oscillations. Since light waves travel very well through a vacuum, the ether hypothesis provided a means other than ordinary material media for supporting these oscillations.

The second reason for believing in the ether was more convincing, and very hard to get around. The ether at rest defined that coordinate system in which light travels with its characteristic velocity, c. This means that if you happen to be moving with respect to the ether, a beam of light will seem to move with velocity either less than c or greater than c, depending on whether you move with the light or against it. This is what is found with other kinds of waves. Sound moves with its characteristic speed with respect to the air. If a wind is blowing, sound will travel faster than usual going downwind, and slower than usual going upwind. This is built into the Galilean transformation given in Chapter I.

So people began, during the latter part of the 19th century, to try to detect the ether. Of particular interest was the question: is the ether at rest with respect to the earth, or is it moving? How fast is the ether wind blowing past us? We might expect off-hand a seasonal variation brought about by the changing direction of the earth's velocity around the sun. Also it would seem possible that the ether might blow stronger on mountain tops, where the earth has less chance to impede the flow. That is why ether experiments were done at different times during the year, and why many were done on mountain tops.

A. The Aberration of Light

A certain effect, known as the aberration of light, was of importance in the ether investigation. This effect had been known ever since 1727, when Bradley[*] observed that the stars seem to perform an annual circular motion in the sky. This apparent motion was understood to be due to the fact that the observed direction of a light ray coming from a star depends on the velocity of the earth relative to the star. The angular diameter of the circular orbits is about 41 seconds of arc, which can be understood by a consideration of Figure 2.1. Because of the motion of a telescope during the time it takes for light to travel down the length of the tube, the light will appear to follow a path which is tilted with respect to the actual path.

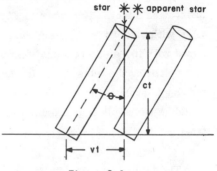

Figure 2.1

The figure shows a star which is straight overhead, being viewed through a telescope. The telescope is mounted on the earth, which is moving to the right with velocity v in the course of its orbit about the sun. The light requires a finite time t to travel down the length of the tube, in which time it covers a distance ct, as shown in the figure. But during this time the telescope has moved to the right a distance vt, as shown. Therefore if the light ray is to strike the eyepiece at the bottom of the tube (rather than the side of the tube), the telescope has to be tilted to the right. The star itself then appears to be in a different position, at an angle θ from the vertical. Six months later, at a time when the star is actually again overhead, the telescope will have to be tilted to the left in order to see the star. More generally, as the earth revolves about the sun the telescope has to be continuously adjusted so as to point slightly in the direction of the earth's motion. Thus as the earth circles the

---

[*] J. Bradley, Phil. Trans. 35, 637 (1728). See also reference 1.

13

sun, the star will appear to move in a small circular path. From the figure, which displays a grossly exaggerated angle θ, it is seen that $\tan \theta = v/c$. Using v = 30 km/sec for the velocity of the earth in its orbit, we have

$$\tan \theta \cong \theta = \frac{30 \times 10^3 \text{ m/sec}}{3 \times 10^8 \text{ m/sec}} = 10^{-4} \text{ radians} \qquad (2\text{-}1)$$

which is about 20.5 seconds of arc. This is in excellent agreement with the observed value (of the circle's radius), as previously quoted.

We conclude from these observations that the ether is <u>not</u> dragged around with the earth. If the ether were at <u>rest</u> with respect to the earth, the telescope could be pointed vertically, so there would be no aberration effect. The ether in Figure 2.1 would then be moving to the right with velocity v, pulling the light ray with it (just as a wind pulls sound with it), so there would be no need to correct for the earth's motion by tilting the telescope. In short, if there <u>is</u> an ether, it must be blowing past us at an average of at least 30 km/sec! Obviously it would be advisable to perform some experiment to see if this is really true!

B. The Michelson-Morley Experiment

In 1887, Michelson and Morley performed a very sensitive experiment in an attempt to detect the motion of the ether. By looking for effects of light interference, they hoped to measure the velocity of the ether wind. The apparatus used was the Michelson interferometer, as shown in somewhat simplified form in Figure 2.2. B and C are fully reflecting mirrors, and A is a half-silvered mirror which reflects half and transmits half of the light incident on it. The idea is this: light from the source strikes A, half of it being reflected up toward B, and the other half transmitted through to C. The light striking mirror B is reflected back, and half of it is transmitted through A to the observer O. The light striking the right-hand mirror C is reflected back, and half of it is reflected off A to observer O. Altogether, half of the light leaving the source reaches the observer, of

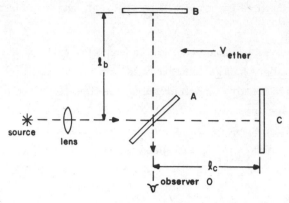

Figure 2.2

which half follows the path ABAO, and half the path ACAO. Since these two paths are generally of different length, the light waves reaching the observer from the path ACAO will be out of phase with those from the path ABAO, so the observer will see interference effects.* The fact that the wavelength of visible light is so small (about 5×10^{-5} cm.) means that there will be a rapid alternation of constructive and destructive interference as the relative path-lengths are changed, an indication that the interferometer is a very sensitive device.

What does the ether have to do with this experiment? Suppose we have adjusted the paths ABAO and ACAO to be of exactly equal length, and suppose the ether is sweeping past the apparatus from right to left with (unknown) velocity v, as shown in Figure 2.2. Then, in going from A to C, the light will have to fight upstream against the ether current, while going back from C to A it will be swept back with the current. The light going from A to B and back to A will be moving largely cross-current, although it will have to fight somewhat against the current or it would be swept downstream and never return to A. We shall see that even if the two paths are of the same length, it takes longer to swim upstream and downstream than to swim cross-

---

*
A brief introduction to the interference of light-waves is given in Appendix H.

current, so the time intervals will be different, and interference can take place.

Recalling that we've assumed light moves with velocity c with respect to the ether, just as sound travels with its characteristic velocity with respect to the air, we can calculate the time needed to traverse each path. In going upstream from A to C, the light will travel at speed c-v with respect to us, and so requires a time $\ell/c-v$. Going downstream from C to A, the speed is c + v, so the time required is comparatively short, $\frac{\ell}{c+v}$. The total time for the trip ACA is therefore

$$\frac{\ell}{c-v} + \frac{\ell}{c+v} = \ell\,\frac{2c}{c^2-v^2} \text{ or finally } t_{ACA} = \frac{2\ell}{c}\,\frac{1}{1-v^2/c^2}. \qquad (2\text{-}2)$$

The time t_{ABA} for the cross-current trip is most easily calculated in the ether's frame of reference, as shown in Figure 2.3. In this frame the ether is at rest, and the apparatus moves to the right with velocity v. During the time $\frac{t_{ABA}}{2}$ the light takes to travel from A to B, the light moves a distance $\frac{ct_{ABA}}{2}$, and the apparatus moves a distance $\frac{vt_{ABA}}{2}$.

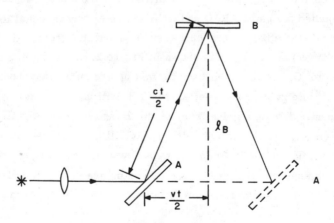

Figure 2.3

Ether at rest, interferometer moving to the right with speed v.

16

From the rule of Pythagoras, we have

$$\ell^2 + (\tfrac{vt}{2})^2 = (\tfrac{ct}{2})^2 \text{ or } t^2 (c^2 - v^2) = 4\ell^2$$

$$\text{or } t_{ABA} = \frac{2\ell}{c} \frac{1}{\sqrt{1 - v^2/c^2}}.$$

(2-3)

Comparing with the upstream-downstream time t_{ACA}, we see that

$$t_{ACA} = \frac{t_{ABA}}{\sqrt{1 - v^2/c^2}}$$

(2-4)

so it takes longer to go up and downstream than to go sideways. Since
we expect that v<<c, it takes a very sensitive device to tell the difference.
The difference in time means that the two light-beams will be out of
phase with each other and consequently will produce interference pat-
terns, even if the path lengths are just the same.

Now in fact with a single measurement it is not possible to separate
the effect of different path lengths from the effect of the ether wind.
Therefore, it is necessary to look at the interference fringes in one position, and then rotate the apparatus by 90° to interchange the position
of the interferometer arms with respect to the ether wind. During the
second measurement the path ACA will be cross-current, and path ABA
will be upstream and downstream.

Michelson and Morley's actual apparatus allowed multiple reflec-
tions so as to increase the path length. The optical system was mounted
on a heavy sandstone slab, which was supported on a wooden float, which
in turn was designed to float in a trough containing mercury. This made
turning easy and smooth, and reduced the effects of vibration. The effective optical length of each arm of the interferometer was about 1100
cm., which would theoretically lead to a shift of 0.4 fringes when the
apparatus was rotated, assuming the ether wind was about the same as
the orbital speed of the earth. From very careful measurements in
July of 1887, they concluded that "if there is any displacement due to

17

the relative motion of the earth and the luminiferous ether, this cannot be much greater than 0.01 of the distance between the fringes."[*]

The simple conclusion from the null result of Michelson and Morley is that the ether is <u>not</u> blowing past us. It must be nearly stationary relative to the earth. It seems incredible that the earth should be so favored, although conceivably there might be a drag effect sufficient to drastically reduce the wind near the earth's surface. But <u>then</u> we are in trouble with the aberration of light. From this effect, as previously discussed, it was concluded that the ether could <u>not</u> be dragged around with the earth. An ether wind of velocity equal to the earth's orbital velocity was needed to explain the small annual circular motion of the stars.

Many other experiments contributed to the confusion surrounding the influence of the ether, such as experiments with light shining through moving water, and measurement of magnetic forces between charged capacitor plates. Naturally several explanations were advanced, some of them very interesting and clever, but none successfully explained all the experimental results.

REFERENCES

1. An interesting account of Bradley's experiments with aberration is contained in "The Discovery of Stellar Aberration" by Albert B. Stewart in the <u>Scientific American</u>, March 1964, p. 100.

2. Two articles on the history of the Michelson-Morley experiment by R. S. Shankland are in the <u>American Journal of Physics</u> 32, p. 16, 1964, and the <u>Scientific American</u>, December 1964, p. 107.

3. Other papers on the experimental basis of relativity are referred to by Panofsky and Phillips in Chapter 14, <u>Classical Electricity and Magnetism</u> (Addison-Wesley, 1955).

---

[*] See reference 2.

18

4. E. T. Whittaker has written a history of the ether, entitled <u>A History of the Theories of Aether and Electricity</u> (Thomas Nelson and Sons, 1951).

5. A biography of Michelson entitled <u>Michelson and the Speed of Light</u> has been written by Bernard Jaffe (Anchor Books, Doubleday & Co., 1960).

PROBLEMS II

1. An artificial earth-satellite completes a 26,000 mile orbit in 90 minutes. Find the angle subtended by the radius of the circle covered by a star as seen from the satellite, due to light aberration.

2. A river is 300 feet wide and flows at 1 foot/second. Two swimmers can each swim at 2 feet/second. One swimmer swims downstream 300 feet and then swims back upstream to where he began, as seen from the shore. The other swims straight across the river and back to where he started on the original shore. Find the time required for each to complete his trip, and verify Eq. 2-4. Remember that the speed of each swimmer is 2 feet/second only in the water's frame of reference.

CHAPTER III
EINSTEIN'S POSTULATES

AS EVIDENCED by many experiments, including light aberration and the results of Michelson and Morley, the ether wind cannot be detected. If there is an ether, it apparently has no influence on physics. No measurements ever made have indicated that it makes the slightest difference what the ether is doing — whether it is at rest or blowing past us. Therefore since we don't observe it, it seems reasonable to discard the idea that it exists. This seems easy to do, and we wonder what all the excitement was about — until we recall that we don't know the frame of reference in which light travels with speed c! The ether frame was supposed to be that frame, but now we don't have it. The ether has vanished along with its frame.

There seems to be no way to find the frame in which light moves with speed c. Various suggestions were put forward: for example, might it not be that light travels at speed c with respect to the source which emits it? The idea that this is the special frame was contradicted by observing the light from double stars. For if at a particular time one star is approaching and the other receding from us as they orbit around one another, light would reach us from the approaching star first. A detailed analysis of this effect shows that the double star system would appear to behave in a different way than is actually observed.[*] (Recent experiments with elementary particle decays appear to provide more conclusive evidence against this "emission theory," as described in reference 4.)

It is here that Albert Einstein appeared on the scene. While working in a Swiss patent office, he published a paper in 1905[**] which set forth the basis of what he later called the special theory of relativity. The theory is founded on two rather innocent-sounding postulates, which are that

---

[*] See reference 3.

[**] "Zur Elektrodynamik bewegter Körper" (On the Electrodynamics of Moving Bodies), Annalen der Physik 17, 1905.

1) Absolute uniform motion cannot be detected.

2) The velocity of light does not depend on the velocity of its source.

Neither statement seems particularly upsetting, but the combination of the two is revolutionary. The first postulate says that motion in a straight line at constant speed cannot be detected — merely meaning that there is no absolute frame with which all motion can be compared. All velocities are relative. There is no "absolute space" or "ether frame" which is at "rest." All we can measure is the velocity of an object in relation to another object. This idea that no inertial frame is to be preferred above any other for viewing physics is certainly not original with Einstein, but is a reaffirmation of the same assumption implicit in Newton's laws, as discussed in Chapter I.

The first postulate implies that the laws of physics must look the same in any inertial frame. If they varied, one frame could be singled out as being fundamentally "better" than another (say because of greater simplicity of the laws), so could become the preferred frame with respect to which all velocities should be measured. We should stress that it is uniform motion which can't be detected, since it is usually easy to tell whether or not you are accelerating, as by watching the behavior of a pendulum or a spring with a mass on the end.* The special theory of relativity deals only with measurements made in inertial frames of reference.

---

* As a matter of fact, if an observer with such "accelerometers" is accelerating at a constant rate, the behavior of the accelerometers will be the same as similar ones in an inertial frame set in a uniform gravitational field. The pendulum will swing and the spring with the mass attached will stretch or compress depending upon how it is oriented. Conversely, such an accelerometer in free fall in a uniform field will give no reading of acceleration at all. As a step in the development of the so-called "general theory of relativity" of 1915, which is a theory about gravity, Einstein postulated that in a restricted region of space no experiment can distinguish between a uniformly accelerated frame of reference and a uniform gravitational field. This postulate is one form of the "Principle of Equivalence," which is further discussed in Appendix D.

21

Since the first postulate is not particularly disturbing, and even seems quite plausible, let us proceed to the second postulate. Denying the idea mentioned previously, it says that "the velocity of light does not depend on the velocity of its source." Some other things in physics have this property, and some do not. For example, if we stand on the sidewalk watching a car go by, and somebody in the car throws a rock straight ahead, the rock's velocity with respect to us will depend on the velocity of the car. In fact, as everybody knows (at least within the limits of experimental error)

$$V_{rock,\ us} = V_{rock,\ car} + V_{car,\ us} \qquad (3\text{-}1)$$

which is just the additive law of velocities. Therefore rocks don't obey the second postulate.

On the other hand, consider the motion of sound in air. It travels at about 1100 ft/sec with respect to the air. Therefore an observer will find that the measured speed of sound has nothing to do with the velocity of the sound-source through the air. Two people in front and in back of a moving car, at equal distances from it when it honks its horn, will hear the honk at the same time. So as long as the velocity of the sound-source is measured with respect to the air, sound is like light in that it obeys the second postulate. The sound velocity is independent of the motion of its source.

But suppose we decide to measure the velocity of the sound-source with respect to the observer. That is, the observer measures the velocity of sound and of the sound-source with respect to himself. Then the situation is quite different. For the speed of sound clearly does depend on the motion of the observer through the air. An observer moving through the air toward a sound-source will measure a sound velocity of greater than 1100 ft/sec, and an observer moving through the air away from the source will measure a sound velocity of less than 1100 ft/sec. Therefore obviously the speed of sound does depend on the source velocity if this source velocity is measured with respect to the observer. Sound obeys Einstein's second postulate in only one special frame of reference, in which the observer is at rest in the air.

22

The crucial difference between sound and light is then immediately clear. Since there is no ether (which would correspond to the air in the case of sound), light has to obey the second postulate in all inertial frames. Without the ether there is no preferred frame to be chosen above any other. The speed of light cannot depend on the source velocity regardless of the reference frame of the observer. It is this fact which produces the first surprise of relativity. Imagine a searchlight out in the middle of empty space, which sends out a continuous beam of light. Some distance away are two spaceships, one at rest with respect to the searchlight and the other moving toward it at relative velocity $c/2$, as shown in Figure 3.1. Observers in both ships are equipped to measure the velocity of light from this searchlight. The "stationary" observers

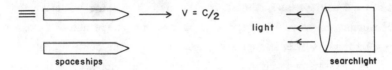

Figure 3.1

will of course measure the velocity to be its standard value of $c = 3 \times 10^8$ m/sec. On the basis of intuition (e.g. from rocks and cars) we might then say that the light velocity measured by the "moving" observers will be $c + v = c + c/2 = 3/2 \times 3 \times 10^8$ m/sec. But then we contradict the postulates of Einstein! For the first postulate states that the situation with the spaceship racing toward the searchlight is exactly the same as if the searchlight were racing toward a stationary spaceship (who can tell which is moving?). But then the second postulate claims that the measurement of light velocity in this latter case must give the same result as if the searchlight source were not moving toward the spaceship. But this result would be just $v_{light} = c$! Our guess of $v_{light} = 3/2$ c for a moving observer was wrong, and should have been $v_{light} = c$. It takes both postulates to force this conclusion. Therefore the velocity of light is independent of the observer's motion. It is the same in every inertial frame of reference. This is a revolutionary idea, unprecedented before Einstein. It took considerable nerve to write down postulates

23

which had as a consequence that light always goes at the same speed no matter how fast the observer is moving.

A particular consequence of the constancy of light's velocity is the following: imagine two sets of rectangular coordinates (inertial frames) which are moving with uniform relative velocity V. At a certain time, the origins of the two systems pass each other, and a bomb explodes at the point where the origins instantaneously coincide, as shown in Figure 3.2. The light from the flash of the explosion will spread out in all directions, the wave-front forming a sphere of radius ct. Observers in one of the two frames will note that the center of this expanding sphere is at the origin of their frame, which is where the bomb went off. But observers in the other frame will find that the center of the sphere is at the origin of their system of coordinates, since the light left that spot at t = 0 and spread out in all directions at the same velocity. In other words, the wave-front forms a sphere in both frames of reference, and the observers in each frame claim that the center of the sphere is at their own origin of coordinates! This appears to be para-

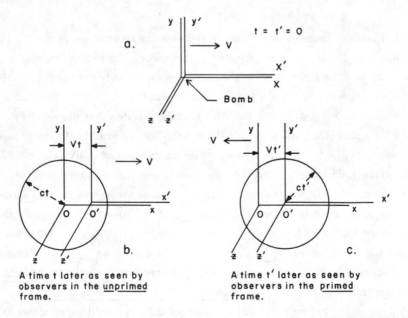

A time t later as seen by observers in the unprimed frame.

A time t' later as seen by observers in the primed frame.

Figure 3.2

24

doxical, since after t = 0 the origins don't coincide. Yet the conclusion is forced by the two postulates.

In order to actually perform this experiment, several observers are needed in each frame. A single observer can't stand back and watch a sphere of light expand. One observer should be located at the frame origin to verify that the explosion happened there at time t = 0. Others can be stationed here and there with synchronized clocks and a knowledge (from measurements with meter-sticks) of how far they are from the origin. If each receives the light flash at time t = r/c, where r is his distance from the origin, they can all compare notes afterwards and be satisfied that the light spread spherically from the origin of their own frame.

So light from the explosion spreads out in such a way that observers in each frame conclude that it spreads spherically, and is centered about their own origin. But how about sound from the explosion? Sound moves with its characteristic velocity only in the frame in which the air is at rest. Only in that frame (say the unprimed frame) will the sound expand spherically with its center at the frame origin. In a primed frame, the sound will spread spherically, all right*, but the sphere center will always be located at the origin of the unprimed frame. So as you might expect, to primed observers the expanding sphere will drift steadily with a velocity equal to the wind velocity felt by them due to their motion through the air. Thus again the great difference between the behavior of sound and light in different frames of reference can be traced to the absence of an ether frame for light.

We've only begun to explore the consequences of Einstein's postulates. Further investigation of time and distances will help to explain how expanding light-spheres can behave in such a paradoxical fashion. From the results of the next three chapters, Appendix F will show how this apparent paradox can be understood.

---

* Approximately, for sound velocities much less than the speed of light. See Chapter V.

REFERENCES

1. Einstein's original paper on special relativity is "Zur Elektro-dynamik bewegter Körper" in the journal Annalen der Physik 17, 1905. A translation is available in the paperback "The Principle of Relativity" by Einstein and others (Dover Publications, 1923).

2. Interesting accounts of how Einstein thought of relativity are contained in his autobiographical notes in Albert Einstein: Philosopher-Scientist, Vol. I, edited by P. A. Schilpp (Harper Torchbooks, 1959) and in a fascinating account of "Conversations with Albert Einstein" by R. S. Shankland in the American Journal of Physics 31, 47 (1963).

3. Reports and discussion on double star data are in articles by Comstock in Phys. Rev. 30, 267 (1910) and by deSitter in Proc. Amsterdam Acad. 15, 1297 (1913) and 16, 395 (1913), and are reviewed in reference 4 below.

4. A review of old and new experiments relating to emission theories and Einstein's second postulate is in an article by J. G. Fox in the American Journal of Physics 33, 1 (Jan. 1965).

PROBLEMS III

1. Do water-waves obey a second postulate in
   a. some frame?
   b. all frames?

2. Devise a way for observers in a given frame to verify experimentally that light spreads out spherically and is centered about their origin, as in the example mentioned in the chapter. Devise a scheme for measuring the shape of the sound wave-front as well.

3. From our conclusion that the speed of light is the same in all frames, show that the analysis of the Michelson-Morley experiment in Chapter II is in error. Show also that if Einstein is correct there should be no fringe shift in the experiment.

CHAPTER IV
TIME DILATION

"until at last it came to me that time was suspect" – A. Einstein

THE PHENOMENON of <u>time dilation</u> follows from the result of Chapter III that light travels at the same speed in all inertial frames. The term "time dilation" means that moving clocks run slow. That is, we will show that if we were to compare the readings of moving clocks with the readings of similar clocks at rest in our own frame of reference, we would find that the moving clocks run behind in time.

To demonstrate this effect, suppose we are sitting in a spaceship in the middle of empty space, and watch another ship go by at some velocity v, as shown in Figure 4.1. On the other ship are two men A and B, across from each other as shown. Each of the two has a clock, syn-

chronized with the other, and the distance between them has been previously measured to be d. Man A suddenly explodes a flashbulb when his clock reads zero, and B measures the time

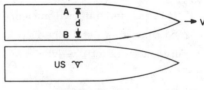

Figure 4.1

at which the light-flash reaches <u>him</u>. He finds of course that this is t' = d/c, since that is what is meant by saying that light travels at speed c. Note that t' is the time interval measured by two clocks <u>on the spaceship</u>.

Now consider what this sequence of events would look like in our frame of reference. To us the ship moves somewhat during the time the light is traveling between A and B, so that to us the light has to go <u>farther</u> than d in order to reach B. In fact, in our frame the light moves along the hypotenuse of a right triangle, as shown in Figure 4.2. One leg of this triangle is the distance d, and the other leg is the distance the ship moves while the light is traveling. The fact that the light moves at an angle in our frame of reference is just the aberration of light effect discussed in Chapter II. A ball thrown from A to B would also move at some angle in our frame, although this angle would be much

27

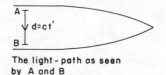

The light-path as seen
by A and B

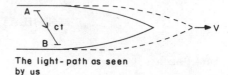

The light-path as seen
by us

Figure 4.2

larger than that of a light-beam because of the ball's slower speed. To us the light travels <u>farther</u> than d, so it must take a longer time to make the trip, since light moves at the same speed in both frames.

If t is the time interval measured by us, the ship will move a distance vt in time t, which is the base of the triangle. The Pythagorean theorem then gives $(ct')^2 + (vt)^2 = (ct)^2$ which can be solved for t' to give

$$t' = t\sqrt{1 - v^2/c^2}. \tag{4-1}$$

Therefore light takes a shorter time, by the factor $\sqrt{1 - v^2/c^2}$, to reach B as measured by A and B than it takes in our frame of reference. This is the same as saying that clocks on the ship (which are used by A and B to measure t') run <u>slow</u> compared to clocks in our frame of reference. For example, if the ship is moving past us at a velocity $v = \frac{3}{5}$ c, and we measure a time interval to be one second, we will observe that the ship clocks advance by only $t' = t\sqrt{1 - v^2/c^2} = \frac{4}{5}$ second. The ship clocks are running slow from our point of view.

It is important to point out the care which would be required to verify this result. How do we measure the time interval in our frame of reference? We should not just sit back and watch A and B, starting and stopping our stop-watch when we see the signal sent and received. For A and B might not be at the same distance from us, so light from them

28

informing us of the sending and receiving would take different times to reach us. This would be an important effect, since the experiment already takes place at the speed of light. Therefore, just as in the length and time measurements discussed in Chapter I, it is necessary to have two observers in our frame of reference, one beside each event. The two observers have previously synchronized their clocks, and the one who is right beside A at the instant the signal is sent records this time as read by his own clock, while the one who is right beside B when the signal is received records the time as read by his own clock. They then compare notes, and the difference in their readings is what we mean by the time interval in our frame of reference.

The formula for time dilation is rather strange for clocks moving faster than the speed of light, since then the factor $\sqrt{1 - v^2/c^2}$ is an imaginary number. If such a clock reads a time t' represented by some real number, it would seem that our clocks should read a time t represented by an imaginary number. This is very difficult to interpret physically, so at least provisionally it would make sense to restrict ourselves to objects moving slower than c. In later chapters the reason for this restriction in relativity theory will become more physically clear. In particular, we will show that no finite force can make a particle move even as fast as light, that a particle moving faster than light would have an energy and momentum given by imaginary numbers, and that if a message were sent from one person to another faster than c, there would exist frames of reference in which the message was received before it was sent!

Needless to say, the experiment with the rocket ship and light-beam is just a thought experiment, which will probably never be done owing to the difficulty of making $\sqrt{1 - v^2/c^2}$ differ appreciably from unity. Fortunately, time dilation has been observed in a different way — namely, in experiments on various kinds of unstable fundamental particles. Such particles can either be created naturally by cosmic rays hitting the atmosphere, or by using high-energy accelerating machines. Each species of unstable particle has a characteristic average lifetime, which can serve as a kind of clock whose rate can be measured as a function of the particle's velocity. For example, there is a particle called the μ-meson, or <u>muon</u>, which decays on the average in a time T = 2.2 x 10^{-6} seconds as measured by clocks in the muon's frame of reference. That is, if we measure the lifetimes of a large number of muons at rest in our frame of reference, their average lifetime will be about 2.2 microseconds. But if a muon moves past us, from our point of view its clock will run slow, so to us it will last <u>longer</u> than T before it decays. More precisely, if a large number of muons all move past us at some velocity v, <u>we</u> will find their average lifetime to be <u>greater</u> than 2.2 microseconds. From their <u>own</u> point of view, with measurements made in their own rest-frame, the muons will decay in their usual lifetime of 2.2 microseconds.

As an example, suppose a particular muon decays in 2.2 microseconds as measured by clocks in its rest-frame. If it moves by us at 4/5 the speed of <u>light</u>, which is <u>not</u> unusually fast for such particles, the dilation factor $\sqrt{1 - v^2/c^2} = \sqrt{1 - (4/5)^2} = 3/5$. Therefore, since t' = 2.2 microseconds, $t = \dfrac{t'}{\sqrt{1 - v^2/c^2}} = \dfrac{5}{3} \times 2.2$ microseconds. This particle lasts 67% longer than a similar particle at rest, as measured in our frame of reference, which means that it will be able to move farther than "expected" before it decays. This feature is very convenient in high-energy experiments, because it means that equipment can be spread out and made in larger sizes than would be necessary if the particles decayed sooner.

Muons are produced in great numbers in the upper atmosphere by the decay of particles called <u>pi-mesons</u>, or <u>pions</u>, which are themselves created in collisions of cosmic-ray protons with air molecules. If these muons actually decayed in their standard average lifetime of 2.2 microseconds from our point of view, they would almost all be gone before reaching the earth's surface. For example, a muon moving at nearly the speed of light would only move a distance of cT = 3 x 10^8 x 2.2 x 10^{-6} = 660 meters, which is considerably less than the height of the atmosphere. A very large muon flux is nevertheless observed, since from our point of view they don't decay that fast. An experiment

30

has recently been carried out by Frisch and Smith[*] to test the time-dilation phenomenon quantitatively. They counted the number of muons at the altitude of Mt. Washington in New Hampshire (6265 feet) and compared this count with the number observed at sea level. Using only muons with speeds between .9950 c and .9954 c, they found by statistical methods that these muons lasted 8.8 ± 0.8 times longer than muons at rest. Theoretically, for muons of these speeds in their detection set-up, they calculated $\dfrac{1}{\sqrt{1 - v^2/c^2}} = 8.4 \pm 2$, so the time dilation effect is in good agreement with experiment.

In the spaceship experiment, we didn't specify what kind of clock was used by the observers. In fact, every moving clock, whether it is a wristwatch, radiating atom, decaying muon, heartbeat, hourglass, or whatever, must run slow. That is, since "time" runs slow, a sensible theory of physics must claim that the various clocks we use to measure time run slow when moving. This is easy to say, but it is often difficult to show in detail why particular clocks run slow, in terms of gears, pendulums, biological processes, and so on.

The simplest clock to analyze, to see how time dilation "works," consists of a mirror and a repeating flashbulb which emits a pulse of light every time light hits it. The clock will "tick" (the bulb will flash) with a time interval $\Delta t' = 2\,D/c$ when it is at rest with respect to us, as shown in Figure 4.3. This interval is the time it takes for the light from the flashbulb to bounce off the mirror and return.

Now suppose the clock moves to the right, or equivalently we run past the clock to the left. Then the light follows the path shown in the right-hand part of the figure, and obviously has to cover a greater distance between ticks.

From Pythagoras we have $\left(\dfrac{c\Delta t}{2} \right)^2 = D^2 + \left(\dfrac{V\Delta t}{2} \right)^2$

or $\Delta t = \dfrac{2\,D/c}{\sqrt{1 - V^2/c^2}} = \dfrac{\Delta t'}{\sqrt{1 - V^2/c^2}} > \Delta t'$. $\qquad$ (4-2)

The clock runs slow by the expected factor.

---

* D.H. Frisch and J.H. Smith, Am. Jour. Phys. 31, 342, 1963.

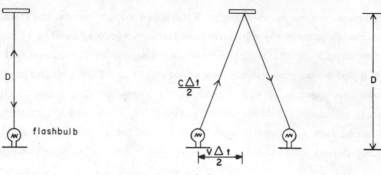

Figure 4.3

The frame of reference in which an object is at rest is said to be the "proper frame" for that object. The "proper time" for the object is the time read by a clock in the proper frame. Thus since a clock is itself an object, a clock measures its own proper time. The proper time between ticks of the flashbulb clock is 2 D/c, while the time between ticks is <u>longer</u> than the proper time when measured in any other frame of reference.

Time dilation is a basic "law of nature" which says that <u>everything</u> moving past you seems to age more slowly than it would at rest. A human being can be viewed as a clock which will "run slow" (age slowly) when moving past you. Your twin brother can travel to the star Sirius and back (a round-trip of 20 light-years) at 4/5 the speed of light, so that you would expect him to be $20/\frac{8}{10} = 25$ years older than when he left. Actually he will only be $25 \sqrt{1 - (4/5)^2} = 15$ years older. So when he returns, he'll be 10 years younger than you, since you've aged the full 25 years in the interim.

This situation gives rise to the so-called "twin paradox, " which has generated a great deal of controversy. If your twin flies away and returns younger than you, why can't he turn the tables and claim that <u>you</u> left <u>him</u> and came back, implying that <u>you</u> should be younger? After all, from Einstein's postulate that absolute motion is undetectable, it shouldn't be possible to tell <u>which</u> twin is moving — everything is symmetrical.

As a first step in the resolution of this paradox, it should be realized that in fact the situation is definitely not symmetrical, and that it is possible to tell which twin went away and came back. In order to leave and return, somebody has to accelerate during a part of the trip. Both brothers will agree as to who accelerates, just by watching their accelerometers (pendulums, say). Einstein's results are only valid for observations made in unaccelerated reference frames, so that the advertised time dilation of moving objects is only true for the experiment as a whole if viewed by the twin who stays at home. We cannot analyze this situation using the time dilation factor if we move with the twin who leaves, because we would then be in an accelerated reference frame.

Using general relativity, or Einstein's theory of gravity, it is possible to analyze the world from accelerated reference frames. Then it is found that another effect, known as the gravitational red shift, slows down accelerated clocks, by just the right amount to give the same result we get by staying with the earthbound twin.[*] The twin who leaves and comes back (and therefore accelerates) is younger than the stay-at-home at the end.

REFERENCES

1. The experiments on muons to check time dilation are described in an article by Frisch and Smith in the American Journal of Physics 31, 342 (1963), and also by Rossi and Hall in the Physical Review 59, 223 (1941).

2. Another experiment related to time dilation is the measurement of the Doppler shift of light from moving sources, which is discussed in Chapter XII. References are listed there.

3. There are innumerable papers on the twin paradox. Some will be listed here, and others can be found in their references:

---

[*] See Appendix E, and for a more complete treatment see C. Møller's The Theory of Relativity, Oxford Press, 1952.

"Some Recent Experimental Tests of the Clock Paradox" by C.W. Sherwin, Phys. Rev 120, 7 (1960).

"The Clock Paradox in Relativity" by C.G. Darwin, Nature 180, 976 (1957).

"Relativistic Observations and the Clock Paradox" by J. Terrell in Nuovo Cimento 16 457, 1960.

"Relativity and Space Travel" by J.R. Pierce in Proc. I.R.E. 47 1053 (1959).

"The 'Clock Paradox' and Space Travel" by E.M. McMillan in Science 126, 381 (1957).

See also Appendix E.

PROBLEMS IV

1. A clock moving at speed $v = \frac{3}{5} c$ reads twelve o'clock as it passes us. In our frame of reference, how far away will it be when it reads one o'clock?

2. The mean lifetime of $\pi^{\pm}$ mesons is about 2.5×10^{-8} seconds in their rest-frame. If a beam of pions is produced which travel on the average 10 meters before decaying, how fast are they moving?

3. A spaceman with 50 years to live wants to see the Andromeda nebula (2 million light-years away) at first hand. How fast must he travel?

4. Two π^{+} mesons are created, one at rest in the laboratory, and the other moving at $v = \frac{4}{5} c$. Each decays in 2.5×10^{-8} seconds in its own rest-frame. Find

    a. the lifetime of the moving pion as measured in the laboratory;

    b. the lifetime of the pion at rest in the laboratory as measured in the frame of the "moving" pion.

CHAPTER V
LENGTHS

AFTER FINDING that time has lost its absolute character, with clocks running at different rates when measured in different frames of reference, we had better be cautious about all kinds of things. Accepting the non-intuitive hypothesis that the speed of light is the same in all inertial frames, many other concepts should be reexamined. For example, might it not also be true that the measurement of distance depends on the observer's frame of reference?

A. Transverse Lengths

In looking back at the discussion of time dilation in the previous chapter, we find that it was actually assumed that distances weren't changed! More precisely, it was assumed that distances perpendicular to the direction of relative motion were the same to both observers, as for example in Figure 4.3, where it was taken for granted that the vertical distance between the flash-bulb and mirror was "D" in both frames of reference.

Fortunately, this assumption that transverse distances are unchanged is correct, as can be seen from a simple thought-experiment. Two men A and B are each equipped with a meter-stick having a thin knife-blade attached to one end, as shown in Figure 5.1. They run toward each other at a high relative speed, holding the sticks perpendicular to the direction of motion with the bottom end barely skimming the ground. If the sticks are really of the same length, the knives should hit each other, but if one stick is longer than the other, it will be sliced off by the knife on the shorter stick. Supposing that each man's stick is exactly one meter long to him, we would like to show that in fact the knives will hit each other, indicating that the stick moving past each man is also one meter long to him. This would prove that transverse lengths are unaffected by motion. That is, from A's point of view his own stick has a length of one meter, but he is not sure that a moving meter-stick (one meter as measured by B) will have the same length. We want to prove that in fact it is.

35

Figure 5.1

The proof follows by contradicting the other alternatives. First suppose that B's stick is <u>shorter</u> than one meter as seen by A. Then B's knife will slice off the top of A's stick. This fact doesn't depend upon who is observing it: it is definitely <u>A's</u> stick (and not B's) which has been cut off. The whole experiment was set up in a symmetrical way, playing no favorites between A or B, but it ends in an unsymmetrical way, with A getting his stick cut off. This can't happen, according to Einstein's first postulate, because it means there is an <u>a priori</u> reason for preferring one reference frame over the other. In such an originally symmetric experiment, with the laws of physics the same for both A and B, everything which happens to A should also happen to B.

The second alternative, that B's stick is <u>longer</u> than one meter as seen by A, implies that B's stick will be cut off, leading to the same contradiction. A preferred frame of reference could again be chosen. The remaining possibility is that the knives will hit each other, which is a symmetrical result, showing that to either observer the meter sticks have the same length. Therefore relativity agrees with our intuition that transverse lengths are unaffected by motion.

B. The Longitudinal Contraction of Lengths

In the situations we've discussed of decaying muons and moving twins, there lurks another effect, showing that <u>longitudinal</u> lengths

36

are affected by motion. We stand on the earth watching muons rain down, passing through several miles of atmosphere even though they ought to be able to go through only about 660 meters. This we interpret as a verification of Einstein's prediction that moving clocks run slow. A meson lasts longer than when it is at rest, which is why it can move so far. But what is going on in the muon's frame of reference? In its rest-frame, the muon decays in the standard time of 2.2 microseconds, so it can't possibly go several miles, even if it is moving at nearly the speed of light! Similarly, from the standpoint of the twin traveling to Sirius, why does the trip seem to take only a comparatively short time? Two possible explanations come to mind:

1. Velocities are not reciprocal — if we measure the velocity of someone with respect to us, he may find a different velocity of us with respect to him. Thus from his own point of view, the traveling twin may be going faster than 8/10c, and the muons may think they're going faster than light!

2. Distances are different in the two frames. A "moving" object may measure the distance it has to go to be less than the distance measured by a "stationary" observer. From the point of view of observers in the muon's frame of reference, the atmosphere would be very thin (< 660 meters high), and the moving twin would find the distance between the earth and Sirius to be less than 10 light-years, by just enough to allow him to complete the journey in only 15 years.

In other words, since by definition velocity = distance/time for any observer, if the time is different for two observers, the velocity and/or distance must be different also. We can't change our ideas about time without changing our ideas about something else also.

Clearly it is the first alternative which must be thrown out, since it contradicts Einstein's first postulate. If the relative velocity between the two objects depends upon which object was measuring it, we would have an absolute way of distinguishing between two frames of reference. We could say that one frame was "better," because the relative velocity was smaller, say, in that frame. This trouble shows up in an extreme form in the mu-meson experiment, where in the muon's frame it would have to move several miles at a speed greater than that of light. Air molecules would therefore be rushing past the muon with speed $v > c$, and their time would be contracted by the factor $\sqrt{1 - v^2/c^2}$, which would be an imaginary number.

According to the second alternative, which is the correct one, the distance of travel is <u>shorter</u> to the moving object. The distance from earth to Sirius as measured by the traveling twin is only $10\sqrt{1 - (8/10)^2} = 6$ light-years! Then, since $t = d/v$, the travel time will be shortened to him by a factor $\sqrt{1 - (8/10)^2}$, which we know to be the case. That is, he will explain the fact that he only requires 15 years to make the round-trip by claiming that the total distance is only $20\sqrt{1 - (8/10)^2} = 12$ light years. So $t = d/v = 12/(8/10) = 15$ years.

This effect is called the "Lorentz-Fitzgerald contraction," proposed independently by these two gentlemen to explain the Michelson-Morley experiment, but the idea was not completely understood and integrated with other relativistic effects until Einstein's theory appeared in 1905. Stately roughly, objects moving past us with velocity v are contracted in their direction of motion by the factor $\sqrt{1 - v^2/c^2}$. Equivalently, if we are moving past something, it is contracted by the same factor when measured in our reference frame. The atmosphere to the cosmic-ray muons is a very thin layer, so that they have plenty of time to penetrate it before decaying. The <u>rest-length</u> of an object is the length measured in the frame which is at rest with respect to the object. In any other frame, the measured length will be <u>shorter</u> than the rest-length. The fact that an object is largest in its rest-frame does <u>not</u> violate Einstein's first postulate, because it does not specify a preferred reference frame. It is true that an object's rest-frame could be taken to be a preferred frame <u>for</u> <u>that</u> <u>object</u>, but a different object might have a <u>different</u> rest-frame, so no overall preferred frame could be specified.

The Lorentz contraction is essential for understanding a "longitudinal flash-bulb clock." Figure 4.3 in Chapter IV showed the "transverse flash-bulb clock," which runs slow by the factor $\sqrt{1 - v^2/c^2}$ when moving. This was just a particular example of the general rule that any clock must run slow by the same factor $\sqrt{1 - v^2/c^2}$ as it moves past an observer with relative velocity v. So now consider the same clock turned 90° with the light going back and forth along the direction of motion of the clock, as shown in Figure 5.2. When at rest, as shown in

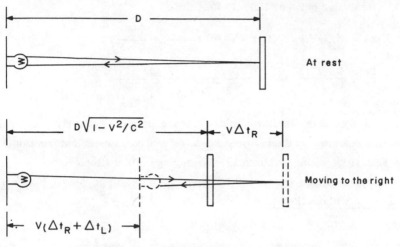

Figure 5.2

the top figure, the time between flashes is $\Delta t' = 2D/c$. When the whole apparatus moves to the right, as in the bottom figure, care is needed in calculating the total light travel-time. While the light moves to the right, before hitting the mirror, it must overcome the distance to where the mirror <u>was</u> when the flash bulb fired (the Lorentz-contracted distance $D\sqrt{1 - v^2/c^2}$), and also the distance the mirror moves in the meantime. If the light requires a time Δt_R to reach the mirror, the mirror will move a distance $v\Delta t_R$ during this time. The total distance the light has to travel to get to the mirror is then

$$c\Delta t_R = D\sqrt{1 - v^2/c^2} + v\Delta t_R,$$

$$\text{giving } \Delta t_R = \frac{D\sqrt{1 - v^2/c^2}}{c - v}.$$

(5-1)

On the return trip, if the light requires a time Δt_L to return to the flash-bulb, the flash bulb will move a distance $v\Delta t_L$ during this time. Therefore the total distance traveled by the light on the return trip is only

$$c\Delta t_L = D\sqrt{1 - v^2/c^2} - v\Delta t_L, \text{ so that}$$

$$\Delta t_L = \frac{D\sqrt{1 - v^2/c^2}}{c + v}.$$

(5-2)

The total time between ticks is therefore

$$\Delta t = \Delta t_R + \Delta t_L = D\sqrt{1 - v^2/c^2}\left(\frac{1}{c + v} + \frac{1}{c - v}\right) =$$

$$\frac{2cD\sqrt{1 - v^2/c^2}}{c^2 - v^2} = \frac{2D/c}{\sqrt{1 - v^2/c^2}} = \frac{\Delta t'}{\sqrt{1 - v^2/c^2}}.$$

(5-3)

This is the same result as for the transverse clock, namely that moving clocks run slow by the factor $\sqrt{1 - v^2/c^2}$. The Lorentz contraction was essential in getting this result, showing again that time dilation and length contraction are part of the same relativistic physics. You can't have one without the other.

We are dealing here with ideas that are not very intuitive, so it is necessary to take some care in describing the measurements necessary to see if a moving object is contracted. Because of the Lorentz-Fitzgerald contraction, we are tempted to say "anything moving looks shorter," which would seem to be a direct consequence. We could presumably see this effect if the velocity of light were small, say 10 meters/second. Then we might think an automobile or a bicyclist going down the street would look squashed up, and a spherical bowling ball would look like an ellipsoid. The joker is in the words "look" and "see," which we have used rather loosely, not being careful to note what kind of measurement the words imply. As a matter of fact, they imply a pretty unsatisfactory method of measurement, even in classical mechanics without any time dilation or length contraction.

As a particular example, suppose a railroad train is moving along a straight track at a velocity approaching that of light. It starts off to our left and moves past us to the right while we stand beside the track looking on. Now at any particular time, the view we get is the sum of all the light reaching our eyes at that time. A "view" is defined by the light simultaneously hitting our eyes. But since some parts of the

40

train are farther away from us than other parts, light will take longer to reach us from some parts than others. Therefore, as the train approaches, light from the caboose must have left before light from the engine did, so that our eyes will receive both light rays simultaneously We see the caboose where it was a long time ago, whereas we see the engine where it was only a short time ago. But a long time ago the train was still far away, so the caboose will appear to be far away, even though the engine is close by! So as the train approaches it will actually look much longer than you might expect. By the same reasoning, it is easy to discover that as the train pulls by and rushes off in the other direction, it will look very short, even shorter than predicted by the factor $\sqrt{1 - v^2/c^2}$.

The apparent stretchings and squashings occur because of the finite speed of light. They would be observed for a fast train even if the world obeyed classical physics, without Einstein. The introduction of relativity has the effect of superimposing a Lorentz-Fitzgerald contraction on these other effects, so that for example a train right beside us (with the engine and caboose equally distant) will be shorter than its rest-length by the factor $\sqrt{1 - v^2/c^2}$.

We have reasoned here on the assumption that a train is essentially a one-dimensional object, and haven't worried about the effects of height and depth. It is very interesting to figure out the appearance of a three-dimensional body moving past, which is taken up in Appendix C. The important thing to remember here is that the Lorentz contraction is found by making simultaneous measurements of the position of the two ends, which is what we usually mean by measuring a length.

As an example of making a careful measurement, suppose we wanted to know the length of a rhinoceros charging rapidly past us. There are various ways we might make an experimental measurement:

1. If we knew the speed of the rhinoceros ahead of time, we could stand to one side with a stopwatch, starting it when the front end of the rhinoceros reaches us, and stopping it when the hind end passes, a time Δt later. We could then say that the length is $v\Delta t$

This won't work unless somebody has already measured his velocity, and the rhino has cooperated by maintaining it. If we are not so lucky, a better approach is method two, which needs more equipment and observers.

2. We can ask a friend, with whom we have synchronized watches (see Chapter VI on how to do that!), to stand a distance from us. If the front end reaches us just as the hind end passes our friend (i.e. our watches read the same), then the length is just the distance between us and our friend. This distance we can measure with a meter-stick any time, either before or after the experiment. The important thing is that we have measured the position of his two ends <u>simultaneously</u>. This has required <u>more than one observer</u>, so that there has been no problem in accounting for light-travel times between the object and the observer.

3. Another thing we might do is take a snapshot of the beast, and measure his size on the film. Taking account of the camera's magnification, and the lateral distance of the rhino from this camera, we can figure out his length. This would be equivalent to taking a quick look at him, noting the angle he subtends, and then computing his size by triangulation. This is obviously an example of a "phony" method, since it measures where his head was at one time and where his tail was at another. Using only a <u>single</u> observer to make a measurement means that light from various parts of the subject require different times to reach him, producing errors in figuring out lengths.

In the following chapters we will be asking how things look to various observers. This should be taken as a shorthand way of asking about the result of careful <u>simultaneous</u> measurements made in the observer's frame of reference, using in general <u>several</u> clocks and <u>several</u> observers in that frame of reference. Except in Appendix C, we won't discuss any more the odd effects brought about by light leaving different parts of an object at different times so as to reach a single observer simultaneously. Our measurements will be of type 1 or 2.

REFERENCES

For more on the visual appearance of moving objects, see **Appendix C**
and references listed there.

PROBLEMS V

1. The disk of the Milky Way galaxy is about 10^5 light-years in diameter. A cosmic-ray proton enters the galactic plane with speed
   $v = .99$ c.
   a. How long does it take the proton to cross the galaxy from our
      viewpoint?
   b. How long does the proton think it takes?
   c. How wide is the galaxy to the proton (in its direction of motion)?

2. A spaceship of rest-length 100 meters passes by the earth at a
   speed such that only $\frac{1}{3} \times 10^{-6}$ seconds is required for it to pass by
   a given point, as measured by clocks on the earth.
   a. How fast is it moving?
   b. How long is the ship from the earth's point of view?

3. Electrons in the Stanford two-mile linear accelerator will reach
   a final velocity of about .9999999997 c. How long would the linac
   be to such an electron? Therefore how much time would it take to
   travel this distance to such an electron (assuming it were to move
   the whole distance at this velocity)? How long would it take the
   electron to make the trip as seen by Stanford?

4. The lifetime of the ρ-meson is about 10^{-23} seconds in its rest-
   frame. If the shortest distance that can be resolved in a photograph of a ρ production process in a bubble chamber is about 10^{-4}
   centimeters, how fast must a ρ go in order for us to see it? How
   far would the ρ think it had gone before decaying?

5. A hole in a table-top is 1" wide. A block of wood which is 1-1/2"
   wide in its rest-frame is shot along the table-top toward the hole
   at a velocity such that it is only 3/4" wide in the frame of the
   table. From the point of view of the table, the block should fall

43

through the hole. But in the frame of the block, the block is 1-1/2" wide and the hole is only 1/2" wide! So how can the block fall through the hole? How can this apparent paradox be resolved? (Appendix A presents a similar problem, also left for the reader to solve.)

CHAPTER VI
SIMULTANEITY

CONTRARY to classical physics and "common sense," the preceding chapters have shown that moving clocks run slow and that moving objects are contracted. But the job of demolition has only begun. Everything in physics must be viewed in the light of Einstein's postulates, either to be possibly modified or even rejected entirely. As we have seen, even concepts which Newton and others thought were a priori and absolute, like space and time, have had to be brought under physical investigation and changed. The topic to be discussed now is more upsetting to most people's intuition than any other conclusion of relativity.

A. The Relativity of Simultaneity

We will find in this section that simultaneity is relative. In other words, if two events are simultaneous in one frame of reference, they need not be simultaneous in some other frame of reference. Suppose for example that two supernovae are born in the universe in different galaxies. Does it always make sense to claim that supernova A blew up first, or would some observers claim that supernova B blew up first? We're not talking about the fact that somebody closer to B might see it explode first, simply because the light from the earlier explosion at A hasn't had time to reach him yet. We suppose that he will correct for this fact.

To answer the question whether simultaneity is absolute or relative, consider the following "experiment": we are calmly sitting in our spaceship in the midst of empty space, when suddenly two other (identical) spaceships approach from opposite directions and pass each other, as shown in Figure 6.1.
Rocket "A" moves to the right, and rocket "B" moves to the left, with equal and opposite velocities as we watch them. Just as they pass, we fire bolts of energy

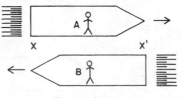

Figure 6.1

at points x and x', which explode between the two ships just as the nose of one reaches the tail of the other. To us, both explosions happen at the same time, so we would say the two events are simultaneous.

But are they simultaneous to the inhabitants of A and B? Suppose there is an observer in the middle of each ship. Each observer <u>knows</u> he is in the middle of his ship, because he has carefully measured his position by using a meter-stick. First consider the man in A. During the time the light from x and x' moves toward him at velocity c, he has moved somewhat to the right, so he will actually see the explosion from x' <u>before</u> that from x. He can therefore say "I'm halfway between x and x', and I saw the light from x' first, so the explosion at x' must have happened earlier than the one at x". On the other hand, the observer on B moves to the left while the light is reaching him, so the light from x gets to him before the light from x', allowing him to say: "I'm halfway between x and x', and I saw the light from x first, so the explosion at x must have happened earlier than the one at x' ".

This result is easy to understand if we watch the whole experiment from the viewpoint of one of the other observers. As seen by the observer in B, rocket A is very short, so if explosion x happens when the nose of B is beside the tail of A, and if explosion x' happens when the nose of A is beside the tail of B, then the two events can't <u>possibly</u> be simultaneous as seen by B. Figure 6.2 shows the rockets in two positions as seen by B.

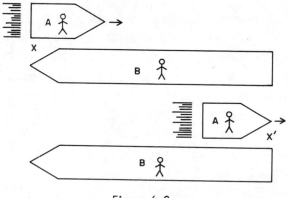

Figure 6.2

46

It is clear that B will claim that event x happened before event x'. In short, the question "which event really happened first?" will be answered differently by different observers. No over-all answer can be given. From A's point of view, explosion x' really happens before explosion x, B's ship is really shorter than A's, and B's clocks really run slow. He knows these things, because he has found them out by careful and well-defined measurements. But he would be cautious not to ascribe his reality to everybody, and would say only that certain facts are correct from his standpoint. From B's point of view, explosion x really happens before explosion x'. From our point of view, the explosions are really simultaneous, but we must admit that A and B have an equal right to do experiments and make conclusions from them, and that they will find the explosions are not simultaneous to themselves.

B. Clock Synchronization in a Single Reference Frame

The outcome of the spaceship experiment indicates that simultaneity is relative, and that clocks in one frame are not synchronized with those in another. In order to understand more clearly how this comes about, we will search for a satisfactory method of synchronizing two or more clocks in a single frame of reference, and then later show that these clocks will not be synchronized to observers in a different frame of reference.

If we are presented with two clocks, at rest with respect to us and separated by a distance D, how can we synchronize them? We will try four different approaches, of which two will turn out to be satisfactory.

1. Let observers be put beside the two clocks A and B. A possible definition of synchronization to the observer beside A would be for both A and B to always read the same, as seen by him. That is, if he looks over at clock B, it will read the same time as his own clock A. The trouble with this definition is that if the clocks are set so that they look synchronized to the observer at A, they will not look synchronized to the observer at B. This definition neglects the fact that the light

47

from clock B requires a time t = D/c to reach A, so that by the time a signal from B reaches A, clock B reads a <u>later</u> <u>time</u>, according to an observer at B. In fact, if observer A uses this definition of synchronization, in which both clocks read the same to him, the observer at B will see clock A lag <u>behind</u> clock B by a time 2D/c, as illustrated in Figure 6.3. With this method, then, observers in the same reference frame

Synchronization according to method 1.

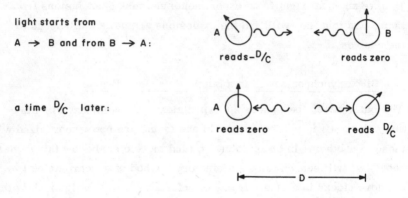

At the time D/c, the observer at A sees that clock A reads t=0, and that B reads t=0, since that is what B read when the light left it. By trial definition no. 1, clocks A and B are synchronized to the observer at A. But the observer at B sees that clock B reads t=D/c, and that A reads t= -D/c, which is what it read when the light left it. Therefore by definition no. 1, the observer at B will claim that the clocks differ by Δt=2D/c, and so are not synchronized to him. An unsatisfactory definition.

Figure 6.3

48

will disagree as to whether or not two clocks are synchronized, making the definition unsatisfactory.

2. If we want to synchronize a lot of clocks, we could begin with them all together, and just set them to read the same. Then we might carry them out to various places, and by definition assert that they are all synchronized. The rather obvious problem with this definition is that the clock readings will depend upon exactly how the clocks are carried to their final locations. The time dilation effect will insure that all the clocks will run slow with respect to a stationary observer, but some will run slower than others, depending upon how fast they are carried, and also for how long a time they are carried. Another group of clocks, synchronized at a different position, and dispersed to the same locations as the first group, will generally disagree with the first group. This method is therefore also an unsatisfactory way of synchronizing clocks.

3. Our next attempt to find a method of synchronizing two clocks will involve taking account of the time needed for signals to pass between them. Let us carefully measure the distance D between clocks A and B. As in the first method an observer is stationed beside each clock, and in addition each observer is equipped with a flash bulb which can be fired. They then agree on the following procedure: When clock A reads t = 0, observer A will set off his flash bulb. The flash will be seen by observer B, who will immediately set his clock to t = D/c, thus accounting for the light transmission time. Clocks A anc B we claim are synchronized. This is an entirely consistent definition, because at any later time t   another flash bulb can be set off by B whose light will reach A at t + D/c, which is what A's clock actually <u>will</u> read when he receives the light.

4. A fourth approach to clock synchronization is the "halfway between" method, which is actually equivalent to method 3. We put two observers with clocks at A and B, measure the distance between them, and put a flash bulb at the halfway point.

Each observer having previously agreed to set his clock to
t = 0 when the flash reaches him, the bulb is fired. The light
will take equal time to reach A and B, so the observers will
be justified in believing their clocks are synchronized. Given
an additional flash bulb, the reader will be able to prove that
methods 3 and 4 are equivalent, so either procedure can serve
as a means of synchronizing two clocks.
Because of the lack of simultaneity in two different frames of reference, we have been very careful in our definition of clock synchronization. We've found that it is possible to synchronize two clocks in the
same reference frame by a straightforward procedure. Since extreme
care is required, it is also necessary to show that it is possible to synchronize three or more clocks in the same frame. Clearly if we can
synchronize clocks A and B, it is also possible by the same procedure
to synchronize clocks B and C. It is left for the reader to convince
himself, using an actual experimental method, that if this is done,
clocks A and C will be automatically synchronized as well. Therefore a well-defined means of synchronizing clocks can be developed, so
that simultaneity is a meaningful idea in a single reference system.
Two events would be simultaneous if the clocks placed beside them read
the same when the events take place. Observers throughout a single
spaceship (in the previous section) can synchronize their clocks, and
agree whether or not two explosions occur simultaneously simply by
comparing the readings of the two clocks on the ship, which are in
proximity to the explosions when they go off.

C. In the Very Process of Synchronizing Two Clocks, a Moving Observer Disagrees

Suppose two clocks A and B, both in the same frame, are synchronized by method 4, the "half-way-between method." A flash bulb
is set off half-way between them, the flash travels toward both clocks
at speed c, and they are both set to t = 0 when the light reaches them.
The process is shown in Figure 6.4. Now suppose we are at rest in
a frame which is moving to the left at uniform velocity v. To us the

clocks move to the right, and the distance between them is contracted to $D\sqrt{1 - v^2/c^2}$. We want to watch, from our frame of reference, the process of synchronizing the clocks. Four stages in this process are shown in Figure 6.5. In our frame of reference, clock A will inter-

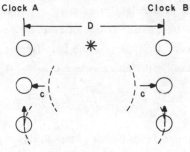

Figure 6.4

cept the flash before clock B, because A is moving toward the light-source, whereas B is moving away from it. Therefore, since the reception of the flash is the cue for each clock to be set to $t = 0$, A will read ahead of B as seen from our frame of reference. Thus in the very process of synchronizing the clocks by the most reliable and well-defined method, they come out unsynchronized to us.

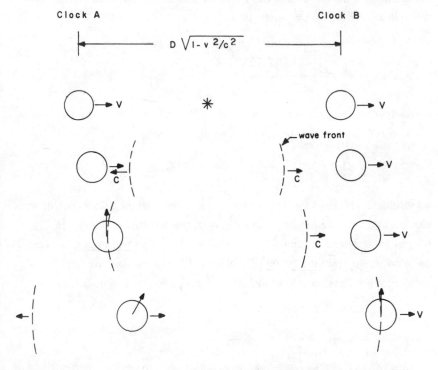

Figure 6.5

51

It is straightforward to calculate how much the two clocks will differ in our frame of reference. To begin with, suppose our clocks read t = 0 just as the bulb fires.[*] At stage three of Figure 6.5, when the light flash meets clock A, our clocks read $t = t_3$, given by

$$ct_3 + vt_3 = \frac{D}{2} \sqrt{1 - v^2/c^2}, \text{ or } t_3 = \frac{D\sqrt{1 - v^2/c^2}}{2(c+v)} \tag{6-1}$$

found from equating the distance between clocks A and the flash bulb at the moment of firing to the sum of the distances traveled by the light and by clock A. At stage four, when the light reaches clock B, our clocks read $t = t_4$, given by

$$ct_4 = vt_4 + \frac{D}{2} \sqrt{1 - v^2/c^2}, \text{ or } t_4 = \frac{D\sqrt{1 - v^2/c^2}}{2(c-v)} \tag{6-2}$$

found from equating the distance the light travels to the sum of the distance between clock B and the flash bulb at the moment of firing, and the distance traveled by clock B.

The time difference between stages three and four is then

$$\Delta t = t_4 - t_3 = \frac{Dv\sqrt{1 - v^2/c^2}}{c^2 - v^2} \tag{6-3}$$

as measured by our clocks. But clock A runs slow to us by the factor $\sqrt{1 - v^2/c^2}$ during this interval, so to us will read

$$\Delta t' = \Delta t \sqrt{1 - v^2/c^2} = \frac{Dv(1 - v^2/c^2)}{c^2 - v^2} = Dv/c^2 \tag{6-4}$$

when clocks B read t = 0. In short, the clocks to us will be out of synchronism by an amount $\Delta t' = Dv/c^2$, with the chasing clock (A in Figure 6.5) reading ahead in time. Note that D is the rest-distance between the clocks, in their direction of motion. Clocks moving along side by side, neither chasing the other, will be synchronized in both frames.

---

[*] That is, our clocks have been previously synchronized, and our clock which is beside the bulb when the flash occurs reads t = 0.

D. A Rocket with Clocks

The results for the reading of clocks and meter-sticks arrived at
so far lead to the following three rules:

1. Moving clocks run slow by the factor $\sqrt{1 - v^2/c^2}$.

2. Moving objects are contracted in their direction of motion by
   the same factor $\sqrt{1 - v^2/c^2}$.

3. Two clocks synchronized in their own rest-frame will not be
   synchronized in other frames, except in those special frames
   in which they are spatially separated only perpendicular to
   their direction of motion. The clock which chases the other
   will read <u>ahead</u> (show a later time) of the clock in front by an
   amount $\Delta t = Dv/c^2$, where D is the <u>rest-distance</u> between
   them along their direction of motion.

As an example of applying these results, picture a rocket of rest-
length 100 meters moving by at a velocity v = 4/5 c. On the ship there
are clocks at the nose and tail, labeled N and T, respectively, which
have been synchronized. On the ground are three strategically placed
clocks, labeled A, B, and C, which are synchronized in our ground
frame of reference. To fix the zero of time, we suppose that our
clock B and the clock N in the nose of the ship both read t = 0 just
as they pass. At this instant, the situation to ground-observers is as
shown in Figure 6.6. The rocket is only $100\sqrt{1 - v^2/c^2} = 100 \cdot \dfrac{3}{5} = 60$
meters long, and our clocks A, B, and C have been placed 60 meters

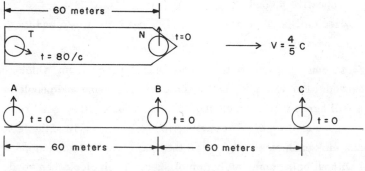

Figure 6.6

53

apart. By rule 3, clock T reads ahead of clock N by $\Delta t = \dfrac{vD}{c^2} = \dfrac{4}{5} \cdot \dfrac{100}{c} = \dfrac{80}{c}$ seconds, with c in meters/second.

Somewhat later the ship reaches clock C, and the tail passes clock B, requiring a travel time $t = \dfrac{\text{distance}}{\text{velocity}} = \dfrac{60}{\frac{4}{5}c} = \dfrac{75}{c}$ seconds. This will be what the ground clocks read, but those on the ship will run slow by the factor $\sqrt{1 - v^2/c^2} = 3/5$, so they will advance by only $\dfrac{3}{5} \times \dfrac{75}{c} = \dfrac{45}{c}$ seconds. Therefore the new situation to ground-observers will be as shown in Figure 6.7. Clock T still reads ahead of clock N by $\Delta t = 80/c$ seconds, as required by rule 3.

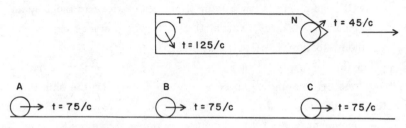

Figure 6.7

The important results are that

a. when clocks N and B pass, they each read $t = 0$ (by definition!),

b. when clocks T and A pass, they read $t = 80/c$ and $t = 0$, respectively,

c. when clocks N and C pass, they read $t = 45/c$ and $t = 75/c$, respectively, and

d. when clocks T and B pass, they read $t = 125/c$ and $t = 75/c$, respectively.

These facts can't depend on the frame of reference from which they are observed. For example, both people on the ground and people on the ship will agree that when clocks T and A pass, they read respectively $t = 80/c$ and $t = 0$. To convince yourself of this, imagine letting the clocks nick each other slightly as they pass, so that each stops running without being completely demolished. Each clock then reads

54

a definite time, and if this is twelve o'clock as seen from one frame, it will be twelve o'clock as seen from any frame.

To make sure that all these results are consistent, we can now try viewing the sequence of events from the standpoint of observers on the ship. To them, the rocket is at rest and has its full rest-length of 100 meters. The ground is rushing past to the left at $v = 4/5$ c, and the three ground-clocks, instead of being 60 meters apart, will be only $60\sqrt{1 - v^2/c^2} = 60 \cdot \frac{3}{5} = 36$ meters apart. So when the nose of the ship and the middle ground-observer meet, the situation to people on the ship is as shown in Figure 6.8.

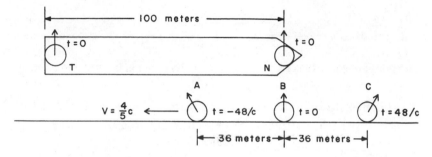

Figure 6.8

As before, clock N and clock B both read $t = 0$ as they pass, since this defines the origin of time for both systems. Clock T must also read $t = 0$, since it is synchronized with clock N on the rocket. The rest-distance between neighboring ground-clocks is $D = 60$ meters, so from rule 3 they will differ in time by $\Delta t = \dfrac{vD}{c^2} = \dfrac{4}{5}\dfrac{60}{c} = \dfrac{48}{c}$ seconds as seen from the ship. Note from the figure that clock C reads a later time than B, which in turn reads a later time than A, since the rule is that chasing clocks read ahead in time.

A while later, clock C passes clock N. This travel time will be $\Delta t = \dfrac{\text{distance}}{\text{velocity}} = \dfrac{36}{\frac{4}{5}c} = \dfrac{45}{c}$ seconds, which will be what the ship clocks read. Each ground-clock will run slow by $\sqrt{1 - v^2/c^2} = 3/5$, so each will advance by only $\dfrac{3}{5} \cdot \dfrac{45}{c} = 27/c$ seconds. The result is pictured in Figure 6.9. Notice that clocks N and C read $t = 45/c$ and $t = 75/c$,

55

respectively, which is the same result found from the point of view of observers on the ground.

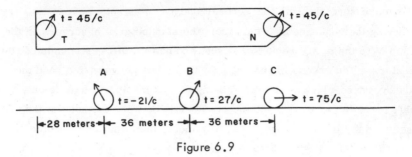

Figure 6.9

The next event takes place when clock A passes the ship's tail. This requires a travel-time $\Delta t = \dfrac{\text{distance}}{\text{velocity}} = \dfrac{28}{\dfrac{4}{5}\,c} = 35/c$ seconds. Then the ship-clocks will read $45/c + 35/c = 80/c$ seconds, and the ground-clocks will advance by an amount $\dfrac{3}{5} \cdot \dfrac{35}{c} = 21/c$ seconds, resulting in the situation shown in Figure 6.10. Note that clocks T and A read $t = 80/c$ and $t = 0$, confirming the result of the ground observers.

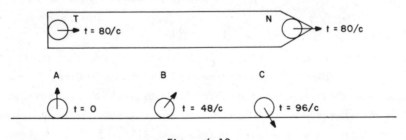

Figure 6.10

Finally, clock B will pass the ship's tail at a time $\Delta t = \dfrac{\text{distance}}{\text{velocity}} = \dfrac{36}{\dfrac{4}{5}c} = 45/c$ seconds still later, so the ship clocks will read $t = 80/c = 45/c = 125/c$ seconds, and each ground-clock will advance by $3/5 \cdot 45/c = 27/c$ seconds, as shown in Figure 6.11. Clocks T and B read $t = 125/c$ and $t = 75/c$, as previously found by observers on the ground.

What we have shown is that even though weird things go on, such as contracted lengths, dilated times, and lack of synchronization of moving clocks, certain facts are independent of the observer's frame

of reference. Namely, the readings of two clocks as they pass each
other will be agreed upon by everybody.

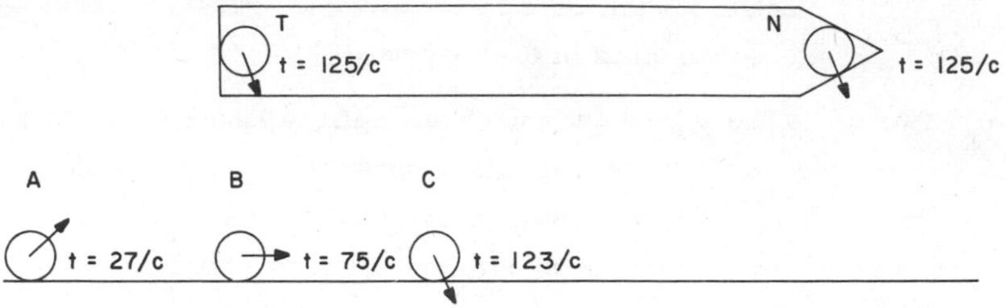

Figure 6.11

PROBLEMS VI

1. Two clocks have been previously synchronized in our frame of ref-
    erence. We stand beside one, and look at the other, which is 30
    meters away. What will it appear to read when the clock beside
    us reads $t = 0$? Now the distant clock is carried to us in 1 second,
    with velocity 30 meters/sec. By how much will the two clocks,
    now side by side, differ?

2. Believing that the sun is about to become a supernova, we blast
    off for Sirius. Just as the journey is half over, we see explosions
    from the sun <u>and also from Sirius</u> at the same instant! Are we
    justified in concluding that in our (the spaceship's) frame of refer-
    ence the two explosions were simultaneous?

3. Show by outlining a conceivable experiment that if clocks A and
    B are synchronized, and if clocks B and C are synchronized,
    then clocks A and C will also be synchronized.

4. A rocket of rest-length 1000 meters moves with respect to us at
    $v = \frac{3}{5}$ c. There are two clocks on the ship, at the nose and the
    tail, which have been synchronized with each other. We on the
    ground have a number of clocks, also synchronized with one an-
    other. Just as the nose of the ship reaches us, both our clock and
    the clock in the noise of the ship read $t = 0$.
    a. At this time $t = 0$ (to us) what does the clock in the tail of the
        ship read?

57

b. How long does it take for the tail of the ship to reach us?

c. At this time, when the tail of the ship is beside us, what does the clock in the tail read?

d. What does the clock in the nose read?

5. Two atoms are at rest one meter apart in the laboratory. A photon is emitted from one, travels at the speed of light, and is absorbed by the other. Show that there is no frame of reference (with $v < c$) in which the emission and absorption are simultaneous.

6. A very long stick ruled with meter markings is placed in empty space. A spaceship of rest-length 100 meters runs lengthwise alongside the stick. Two spacemen equipped with knives and synchronized watches station themselves fore and aft. At a prearranged time, each reaches through a porthole and slices through the stick. If the relative velocity of the stick and ship is $\frac{4}{5}$ c, how many meter marks are on the cut-off portion of the stick? Is this result consistent with what is seen in the frame of the stick?

CHAPTER VII
THE LORENTZ TRANSFORMATION

LET US NOW systematically explore how the coordinates of an event in one reference frame are related to the coordinates of the same event in a different reference frame. In particular, we set up two systems of coordinates which have x-axes in common, and are moving with relative velocity V in the x-direction. Using the same conventions introduced in Chapter I, we will call these two sets of coordinates S   and S', with S' moving to the right, as shown in Figure 7.1.

Now it is obvious from the results of relativity so far that the Galilean transformation (1-1) given in Chapter I

$$x' = x - Vt$$
$$y' = y$$
$$z' = z \qquad\qquad (7\text{-}1)$$
$$t' = t$$

can't be correct. The equations predict that lengths and time intervals don't depend on the observer's frame of reference, and that two events simultaneous in one frame are simultaneous in <u>all</u> frames. Also the Galilean velocity transformation $v_x' = v_x - V$ predicts that light will go at different speeds in different frames,

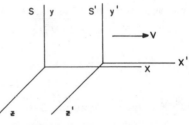

Figure 7.1

because we can take the special case of a light wave traveling with $v_x = c$. We would <u>like</u> to find a transformation which is <u>compatible</u> with the phenomena of length contraction, time dilation, and all the other results obtained so far.

A. Derivation of the Lorentz Transformation

The correct transformation is called the <u>Lorentz transformation,</u> and we can derive it from our knowledge of time dilation and the

Lorentz-Fitzgerald contraction. We use the set of axes shown above, with S' moving to the right. The two clocks at the origins are set to $t = t' = 0$, just as the origins coincide. Sometime later, a flashbulb goes off with coordinates (x, y, z, t) in S, and (x', y', z', t') in S'. The situation is shown in Figure 7.2.

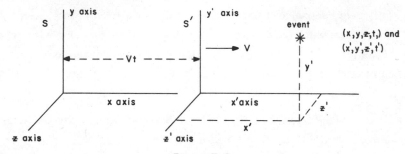

Figure 7.2

We will first try to find x in terms of x'. From the diagram, we see that the origins of the two systems are separated by a distance Vt according to observers in frame S. Also to observers in S, the distance x' will be contracted by the factor $\sqrt{1 - V^2/c^2}$. That is, observers in S' say the x-distance from their origin to the event is x', but observers in S measure it to be only $x' \sqrt{1 - V^2/c^2}$. So we then have $x = Vt + x' \sqrt{1 - V^2/c^2}$, or, solving for x',

$$x' = \frac{x - Vt}{\sqrt{1 - V^2/c^2}} \, . \qquad (7-2)$$

This is the same as the Galilean equation, except for the factor $\sqrt{1 - V^2/c^2}$, which is almost unity for small velocities.

There is no contraction of the y and z coordinates, because they are perpendicular to the direction of motion, so the next two equations of the Lorentz transformation are $y' = y$ and $z' = z$, which are the same as for the Galilean transformation.

Finally we come to the time transformation, which we expect to be more interesting than the old $t' = t$ equation. We will get this by going clear back to the pictures of the expanding spheres of light in Chapter III. A flash bulb goes off from the origins of S and S' just as they

60

pass, and the light spreads out in a sphere in each system of coordinates. In the S-frame, the equation of the sphere's surface is $x^2 + y^2 + z^2 = c^2 t^2$. That is, the radius of the sphere is ct. In the S' frame, the equation of the sphere's surface is $(x')^2 + (y')^2 + (z')^2 = c^2 t'^2$.
So

$$(x')^2 + (y')^2 + (z')^2 - c^2(t')^2 = 0 = x^2 + y^2 + z^2 - c^2 t^2. \qquad (7\text{-}3)$$

But $y' = y$, and $z' = z$, so we are left with $(x')^2 - c^2(t')^2 = x^2 - c^2 t^2$.
We also know that $x' = \dfrac{x - Vt}{\sqrt{1 - V^2/c^2}}$, so $\dfrac{(x-Vt)^2}{1 - V^2/c^2} - x^2 + c^2 t^2 = c^2(t')^2$.

Doing a little algebra, we have $t' = \dfrac{\left\{ (x-Vt)^2 - (x^2 - c^2 t^2)(1 - V^2/c^2) \right\}^{\frac{1}{2}}}{c \sqrt{1 - V^2/c^2}}$

or

$$t' = \frac{t - Vx/c^2}{\sqrt{1 - V^2/c^2}} \ . \qquad (7\text{-}4)$$

Collecting all our results, we have the complete Lorentz transformation

$$\boxed{\begin{aligned} x' &= \frac{x - Vt}{\sqrt{1 - V^2/c^2}} \\ y' &= y \\ z' &= z \\ t' &= \frac{t - Vx/c^2}{\sqrt{1 - V^2/c^2}} \end{aligned}} \qquad (7\text{-}5)$$

which can be more compactly written by defining $\gamma = \dfrac{1}{\sqrt{1 - V^2/c^2}}$:

$$\boxed{\begin{aligned} x' &= \gamma\,(x - Vt) \\ y' &= y \\ z' &= z \\ t' &= \gamma\,(t - Vx/c^2) \end{aligned}} \qquad (7\text{-}6)$$

As we expected, time has gotten mixed up. Note that as $V/c \to 0$ (small velocities) these equations reduce to the Galilean transformation. Let us check these equations to see if they agree with what we know. We stand side by side with a friend in frame S, equipped with synchronized watches and a high-speed rhinoceros, who is moving at speed V with respect to us, but is at rest in system S'. Let x_1 be our measurement of his head in the S-frame at time t, and x_1' be the position of his head in his own frame S'. Furthermore, x_2 will be our measurement of his tail at the same time t, and x_2' will be the position of his tail in S'. Then the difference $x_1 - x_2$ will be his apparent length to us, and $x_1' - x_2'$ will be his rest-length "L_o". So

$$L_o = x_1' - x_2' = \frac{x_1 - Vt}{\sqrt{1 - V^2/c^2}} - \frac{x_2 - Vt}{\sqrt{1 - V^2/c^2}} = \frac{x_1 - x_2}{\sqrt{1 - V^2/c^2}} \quad . \quad (7\text{-}7)$$

Thus the apparent length is $x_1 - x_2 = L_o \sqrt{1 - V^2/c^2}$, and he is contracted, as expected.

Now let's check to see that moving clocks run slow. Take the clock at the origin of the S' system, which read $t' = 0$ when it passed the origin of the S system. We will stand in the S frame and look at this clock at a time t later. It has moved a distance $x = Vt$, but (since it is at the S' origin) x' is always zero. So we have

$$t' = \frac{t - Vx/c^2}{\sqrt{1 - V^2/c^2}} = \frac{t - (V/c^2)Vt}{\sqrt{1 - V^2/c^2}} = \frac{t(1 - V^2/c^2)}{\sqrt{1 - V^2/c^2}} = t\sqrt{1 - V^2/c^2}. \quad (7\text{-}8)$$

That is, t' reads less than it "should" by the factor $\sqrt{1 - V^2/c^2}$, so we would say that the primed clock is running slow.

We can also derive the rule that "chasing clocks read ahead in time," or more precisely that given two clocks moving past us with velocity v, one behind the other, in our frame of reference the one behind will read a time $v D/c^2$ later than the one in front, as shown in Figure 7.3. Here D is the rest-distance between the clocks, which corresponds to a distance $D \sqrt{1 - v^2/c^2}$ in our frame of reference, owing to the

62

Lorentz contraction. We've
assumed of course that the two
clocks have been synchronized
in their own frame of reference.

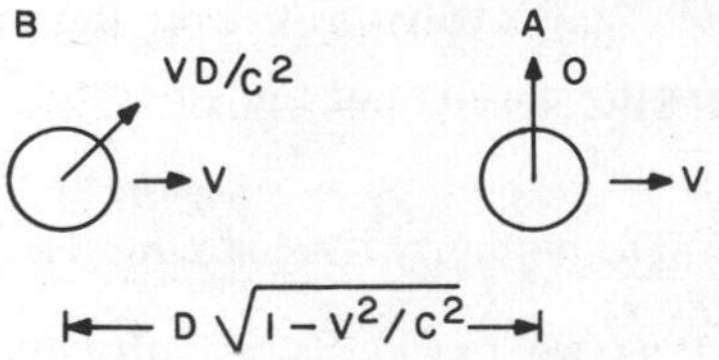

Figure 7.3

Suppose we're observing from
the unprimed frame, and the
two clocks A and B are at rest on the x'-axis of the primed frame.
A is in front of B a distance D in their rest-frame, or $D\sqrt{1-v^2/c^2}$
in our frame. At a particular time t in our frame, the Lorentz transformation says that clock A will read time $t_A' = \gamma(t-Vx_A/c^2)$ and clock
B will read time $t_B' = \gamma(t-Vx_B/c^2)$ where x_A and x_B are the positions of A and B in the unprimed frame. The difference in time read
by A and B is then

$$t_B' - t_A' = \frac{\gamma V}{c^2}(x_A - x_B) = \frac{VD}{c^2} \qquad (7\text{-}9)$$

since the distance in our frame is $(x_A - x_B) = D\sqrt{1-v^2/c^2} = D/\gamma$. This
shows that the Lorentz transformation can reproduce all of the rules we
derived previously by other means. Instead of remembering the rules
of time dilation, length contraction, and the difference in moving clock
readings, the Lorentz transformation equations can be used to compare
measurements in two frames.

It is possible to write the Lorentz transformation for the unprimed
variables in terms of the primed variables, which is called the inverse
transformation. It is

$$
\begin{aligned}
x &= \frac{x' + Vt'}{\sqrt{1 - V^2/c^2}} = \gamma(x'+Vt') \\[2mm]
y &= y' \\
z &= z' \\[2mm]
t &= \frac{t' + Vx'/c^2}{\sqrt{1 - V^2/c^2}} = \gamma(t'+V x'/c^2)
\end{aligned}
\qquad (7\text{-}10)
$$

which just involve switching the primed and unprimed variables and changing the sign of the velocity.

B. The Velocity Transformation

Just as we found the velocity transformation for Galilean relativity, we can find the velocity transformation for Einstein's relativity, by using the Lorentz transformation. Namely,

$$v_x{}' \equiv \frac{dx'}{dt'} = \frac{\dfrac{dx - Vdt}{\sqrt{1 - V^2/c^2}}}{\dfrac{dt - Vdx/c^2}{\sqrt{1 - V^2/c^2}}} = \frac{\dfrac{dx}{dt} - V}{1 - \dfrac{V}{c^2}\dfrac{dx}{dt}} \equiv \frac{v_x - V}{1 - Vv_x/c^2} \ .$$

Also

$$v_y{}' \equiv \frac{dy'}{dt'} = \frac{\dfrac{dy}{dt - Vdx/c^2}}{\sqrt{1 - V^2/c^2}} = \frac{\dfrac{dy}{dt}\sqrt{1 - V^2/c^2}}{1 - (V/c^2)\dfrac{dx}{dt}} \equiv \frac{v_y\sqrt{1 - V^2/c^2}}{1 - Vv_x/c^2}$$

and by the same procedure $\quad v_z{}' = \dfrac{v_z\sqrt{1 - V^2/c^2}}{1 - Vv_x/c^2} \ .$

Collecting them all together, we have found that

$$
\boxed{
\begin{aligned}
v_x{}' &= \frac{v_x - V}{1 - Vv_x/c^2} \\[2ex]
v_y{}' &= \frac{v_y\sqrt{1 - V^2/c^2}}{1 - V v_x/c^2} \qquad \text{and} \\[2ex]
v_z{}' &= \frac{v_z\sqrt{1 - V^2/c^2}}{1 - V v_x/c^2} \ .
\end{aligned}
}
\tag{7-11}
$$

The corresponding inverse transformation is

64

$$v_x = \frac{v_x' + V}{1 + V v_x'/c^2}$$

$$v_y = \frac{v_y' \sqrt{1 - V^2/c^2}}{1 + V v_x'/c^2}$$

$$v_z = \frac{v_z' \sqrt{1 - V^2/c^2}}{1 + V v_x'/c^2}.$$

The velocity transformation is very interesting. The equation for v_x' differs from the Galilean "intuitive" equation by the denominator $1 - Vv_x/c^2$. The equations for v_y' and v_z' have this same denominator, and also have the factor $\sqrt{1 - V^2/c^2}$ in the numerator. These extra factors in the transformation equations can be thought of as arising from length contraction and time dilation, which we would expect to affect the measurement of velocities. Again, of course, these equations reduce to the ordinary, non-relativistic Galilean velocity transformation as $V/c \to 0$.

Let us explore these equations, using them in some examples to see if they predict any new effects. We had first better make sure that light will have the same velocity in every frame, to check the consistency of our results. First take a light beam in the x-direction, having $v_x = c$, $v_y = v_z = 0$. We then find from the equations that

$$v_x' = \frac{c - V}{1 - Vc/c^2} = c, \quad v_y' = 0, \quad v_z' = 0. \tag{7-12}$$

So far so good. The light travels in the x-direction in the primed frame also, with the same velocity c. Next take a beam in the y-direction, having $v_y = c$, $v_x = v_z = 0$. Then we calculate

$$v_x' = \frac{-V}{1 - 0} = -V,$$

$$v_y' = \frac{c\sqrt{1 - v^2/c^2}}{1 - 0} = c\sqrt{1 - v^2/c^2}, \quad v_z' = 0. \tag{7-13}$$

So in the S' frame the beam is not moving along the y' axis, which is not very surprising, because since it travels at right angles to the motion of the primed frame, it must travel at some angle to the y' axis. This is just the aberration of light effect discussed in Chapter II, similar to watching rain fall toward the ground while in a moving car. The velocity of the light is still c, however, because

$$v' \equiv \sqrt{(v_x')^2 + (v_y')^2 + (v_z')^2} = \sqrt{v^2 + c^2\,(1 - V^2/c^2)} = c \qquad (7\text{-}14)$$

which is illustrated in Figure 7.4.

As another example, suppose a bullet moves in the x-direction at 2000 meters/sec with respect to the ground. Then you run along in the same direction at 500 meters/second, carrying with you enough equipment to measure the bullet's
speed with respect to you (say
with a radar set). Before relativity, you would have confidently
predicted that you would measure the bullet to be moving 1500

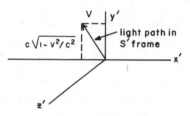

Figure 7.4

meters/second, a direct result of the Galilean velocity transformation or the law of vector addition of velocities. But in actual fact, calling your frame the primed frame, you would measure

$$v_x' = \frac{v_x - V}{1 - Vv_x/c^2} = \frac{2000 - 500}{1 - \dfrac{(500)\,(2000)}{9 \cdot 10^{16}}} = \frac{1500}{1 - 1.11 \cdot 10^{-11}}$$

$\cong$ 1500.000000017 meters/second as the speed of the bullet with respect to you.

The most interesting application of the velocity transformation is to show that no object can go faster than the speed of light. Actually, we should qualify this, and say that if a particle is traveling at some velocity v < c in a particular reference frame, it will travel at v' < c in any other reference frame. Of course, our second reference frame must not go with speed V > c relative to the first, because then

66

the famous factor $\sqrt{1 - V^2/c^2}$ would become imaginary, which makes no sense. Lengths and times, instead of being contracted and dilated, would become imaginary, which is difficult to interpret physically.

As a particular example, picture two rhinoceroses destined for a head-on collision at fantastic velocities. That is, one rhinoceros (A) approaches from the left at $v = .99c$, and another (B) approaches from the right with $v = -.99c$ (the minus sign referring to the fact that B is running to the left). We want to ask the question: "What is the velocity difference between A and B?" The answer is simple in the old Galilean relativity. The difference in their velocity would be $1.98c$, regardless of the reference frame in which the events are viewed. But in Einsteinean relativity, we have to be careful to specify the observer's frame of reference. If we stand on the ground, with the beasts approaching one another, each at $.99c$, the difference in the velocities is $1.98c$, by definition. Of course there is no object moving at this velocity. But now take the point of view of one of the two rhinos. In his frame of reference, the difference in their velocities is just the velocity of the other rhinoceros.

Let the ground be the S-frame, in which rhinoceros A runs up the -x axis toward the origin at $.99c$, and B runs down the +x axis toward the origin at $-.99c$. Then for rhinoceros B, $v_x = -.99c$, $v_y = v_z = 0$. Choose the S' frame to be moving with rhinoceros A to the right: i.e., A is at rest in S'. Therefore the velocity of B with respect to A will simply be B's velocity in the S' frame, which is v_x'. So, since V (the relative velocity between frames S and S') is $.99c$, we have

$$v_x' = \frac{v_x - V}{1 - Vv_x/c^2} = \frac{-.99c - (.99c)}{1 - \frac{(.99c)(-.99c)}{c^2}}$$ (7-15)

$$= \frac{-1.98c}{1 + (.99)^2} \cong -.99995 \, c.$$

The result is a difference in velocity which is less than c. This is illustrated in Figure 7.5, showing again that velocities are not additive.

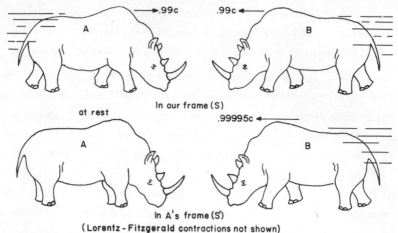

In our frame (S)

at rest

.99995c ←

In A's frame (S')
(Lorentz - Fitzgerald contractions not shown)

Figure 7.5

To calculate the velocity of an object in various frames it is necessary to use the Lorentz velocity transformation.

The relativistic velocity transformation was tested inadvertently by H. L. Fizeau in 1851.[*] At the time, he was trying to find out whether moving water tended to drag light along with it. He knew that light travels more slowly in materials than in vacuum, which is usually expressed by writing the velocity as $v = c/n$ where n is the "index of refraction" of the particular substance. This velocity is measured in the rest-frame of the material, but could clearly be different in another frame of reference. The material provides a preferred reference frame, so a different velocity in another frame should not be surprising.

It would be natural to think that flowing water might tend to "drag" light along with it, so that if a light-beam were sent through a column of water in the direction of flow it would have a laboratory velocity of

$$v_{light} = \frac{c}{n} + \alpha v_{water} \qquad (7\text{-}16)$$

where α is a "dragging coefficient." If $\alpha = 1$, then moving water would drag the light right along with it. Light opposing the flow would be

---

[*] H. L. Fizeau Comptes Rendus 33 349 (1851).

slowed somewhat, to a laboratory speed of

$$v_{light} = \frac{c}{n} - \alpha v_{water}. \tag{7-17}$$

The calculation of the dragging coefficient is a simple exercise in using the velocity transformation. Suppose water is flowing to the right in the laboratory, and light is shone through it in the same direction. Then by the usual conventions, the water-frame is the primed frame, and the laboratory is the unprimed frame. By the velocity transformation,

$$v_x = \frac{v_x' + V}{1 + v_x' \frac{V}{c^2}}, \text{ where } V \text{ is the water's velocity. But } v_x' = c/n, \text{ so}$$

$$v_x = \frac{\frac{c}{n} + V}{1 + V/cn} \cong (\frac{c}{n} + V)(1 - \frac{V}{cn}) \text{ using the binomial expansion on the de-}$$

nominator, since $\frac{V}{cn} \ll 1$. Neglecting the V^2/cn term,

$$v_x \cong \frac{c}{n} + (1 - \frac{1}{n^2}) V \tag{7-18}$$

for water velocities much less than the speed of light.

Thus relativity predicts a dragging coefficient of $\alpha = (1 - \frac{1}{n^2})$ which for water (n = 4/3), amounts to $\alpha = 7/16 = .438$. For light moving to the left in the same flow of water, the light velocity is $v_x' = -c/n$ in the water (primed) frame, so

$$v_x = \frac{-c/n + V}{1 - V/cn} \cong \frac{c}{n} - (1 - \frac{1}{n^2}) V \tag{7-19}$$

agreeing with our expectation.

Fizeau carried out a sensitive interference experiment using a circulating water channel shown schematically in Figure 7.6. As in Michelson's experiment, the light from the source was split up into two beams by a half-silvered mirror, one beam traveling clockwise and the other counterclockwise in the figure. After recombining, the beams interfere with each other, showing fringes. This interference pattern is present even when the water in the channel is at rest. But when the flow is set up, the clockwise beam moves faster than the counterclockwise

69

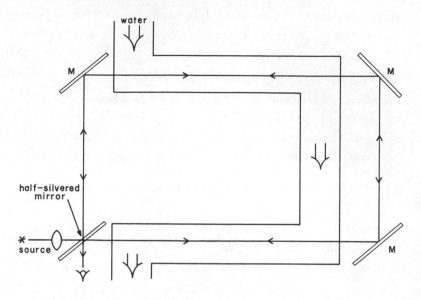

Figure 7.6

beam, since it is moving in the same direction as the water. Thus the phase difference is not the same as when the water is at rest, and the interference fringes shift. The extent of the fringe shift is a measure of the dragging coefficient α. Michelson and Morley[*] repeated Fizeau's experiment with improved apparatus in 1886, and obtained a dragging coefficient of $\alpha = .434 \pm .02$, in good agreement with the relativistic prediction derived twenty years later.

The Lorentz transformation summarizes all the results of special relativity arrived at so far. It contains within it the rules for how positions, times, velocities, and accelerations change from one inertial frame to another. Now since fundamental laws of physics depend upon some or all of these quantities, the Lorentz transformation (along with the corresponding transformations for velocity, acceleration, and other variables aside from position and time) tells us how to write the laws in one inertial frame in terms of the laws in another inertial frame. But a consequence of Einstein's first postulate was that the

---

[*] Michelson and Morley, American Journal of Science 31, 377 (1886).

fundamental laws must look the same in any inertial frame, as pointed out in Chapter III. Otherwise some frames could be preferred over others. Therefore, we can now say that all fundamental laws of physics should be invariant under the Lorentz transformation. This means that if we transform variables from one frame to another by using the Lorentz transformation (and the other relativistic transformations derived from it) the laws must look just the same. With the following chapter on relativistic momentum, we begin to search for the fundamental laws of relativistic dynamics, including conservation of momentum and energy, and the equation of motion.

REFERENCES

1. Einstein's derivation of the Lorentz transformation is in his article "On the Electrodynamics of Moving Bodies" translated in the paperback The Principle of Relativity by Einstein and others (Dover Publications 1923). Previous articles by H. A. Lorentz are in the same book.

2. More discussion of Fizeau's experiment is contained in many of the standard texts on relativity listed in the bibliography at the end of this book.

3. Chapter XIII takes up the Lorentz transformation again as a rotation in spacetime.

PROBLEMS VII

1. A clock moving past us at speed $v = \frac{c}{2}$ reads $t' = 0$ when our clocks read $t = 0$. Using the Lorentz transformation, find out what our clocks will read when the moving clock reads $t' = 10$ seconds.

2. Two clocks attached to the x' axis at $x' = 0$, and $x' = 1$ meter in the primed frame move past us to the right at speed $v = \frac{3}{5} c$. The clock at $x' = 0$ reads $t' = 0$ just as it passes our origin $x = 0$ at $t = 0$. Find

    a. The x-coordinate (our frame) of the other clock at $t = 0$.

    b. The reading of the other clock at $t = 0$.

3. A rocket of rest-length 100 meters moving at speed $v = \frac{3}{5} c$ contains a spaceman at the tail of the ship. He fires a bullet toward the front of the ship, which travels at $v = \frac{3}{5} c$ with respect to him.

   a. How fast is the bullet moving with respect to us?

   b. How long does the ship appear (1) to us? (2) to the spaceman? (3) to the bullet?

   c. How much time does it take for the bullet to reach the front of the ship, as measured by (1) us? (2) the spaceman? (3) the bullet?

4. A K^o-meson moves past us to the right at speed $v = c/2$. In the K^o rest-frame, it decays into two $\pi^{o'}$s, one going straight "up," and the other straight "down," with equal and opposite velocities v_π^o.

   a. In terms of v_π, how fast will the π's be moving in the laboratory?

   b. At what angle will they move with respect to the vertical?

5. A π^+-meson moves to the right at $v = \frac{4}{5} c$. In the π^+ rest-frame, it decays into a neutrino, moving to the right with speed c, and a muon, moving to the left with speed v_μ.

   a. How fast does the neutrino move in the laboratory?

   b. In terms of v_μ, how fast does the muon move in the laboratory?

6. By taking a derivative of the velocity transformation equations, one can obtain transformation laws for acceleration. Show in this way that the x-components of acceleration as measured in two frames are related by $a_x' = \dfrac{a_x}{\gamma^3 (1-v_x V/c^2)^3}$. Therefore unlike Galilean relativity, the acceleration of an object depends upon the inertial frame in which it is measured.

CHAPTER VIII

RELATIVISTIC MOMENTUM

CLASSICAL MECHANICS is based on Newton's laws of motion, and in particular the second law, which is $\vec{F} = m\vec{a}$ for a particle of mass m. As mentioned in Chapter I, Galilean relativity is solidly entrenched in this law. The equation $\vec{F} = m\vec{a}$ looks the same in two inertial reference frames if the Galilean transformation is used to transform variables between the two frames. But what if the <u>Lorentz</u> transformation is used instead? Is the equation $\vec{F} = m\vec{a}$ <u>still</u> the same in all inertial frames? If not, it cannot be the correct equation of motion. For then not all inertial frames would be equally good for the description of physics, which would violate Einstein's first postulate. So if $\vec{F} = m\vec{a}$ is not invariant under the Lorentz transformation, we will have to search for <u>another</u> equation of motion which <u>can</u> withstand the test of relativity.

It is not difficult to find the way in which <u>acceleration</u> transforms in Einstein's theory. It is only necessary to take a time derivative of the velocity transformation (7-11) given in Chapter VII, as suggested in Problem 7-6. On the other hand, there is no clear way to discover how the <u>force</u> changes from one frame to another. It doesn't change at <u>all</u> in non-relativistic mechanics, but after what we've been through so far, we suspect that this fact doesn't have much bearing on the relativistic situation! If we knew an expression for <u>some</u> relativistic force, we could test it out to see how it transforms. But so far we don't, so we'll temporarily back off from the question, and then return to it in Chapter XIV.

In order to tackle relativistic dynamics, we'll have to try something simpler than the search for an equation of motion. So let's begin by trying to find out what <u>momentum</u> is like in relativity. We can define "momentum" to be anything we like, but it makes sense to endow it with the following properties:

1. Momentum should be a <u>conserved</u> quantity, in the same sense that the classical momentum $\vec{p} = m\vec{v}$ is conserved.

73

2. The relativistic momentum should reduce to $\vec{p} = m\vec{v}$ for low velocities.

The restriction that momentum be <u>conserved</u> suggests that we investigate a collision process of some kind, for we can then compare various quantities before and after the collision to see which ones remain the same. In particular, suppose there are two people A and B who are moving with respect to each other with a uniform velocity V in the x-direction, and are separated somewhat in the y-direction. At the proper moment they each throw a ball in the y-direction so that the balls collide in a symmetric fashion. Figure 8.1 shows two views of the collision. The first diagram shows what is seen by observer A. He throws his ball straight "down" with speed u, and it hits B's ball and bounces back to him with speed -u. The second diagram shows what is seen by B. He throws his ball straight "up" with speed u, which then bounces straight back to him after colliding with A's ball. With our usual conventions, we can say that A is at rest in the unprimed (S) frame, and that B is at rest in the primed (S') frame.

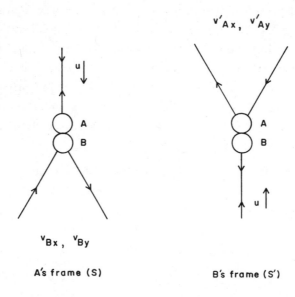

A's frame (S)   B's frame (S')

Figure 8.1

74

Using the relativistic velocity transformation (7–11), we can find the unknown quantities v_{Bx}, v_{By}, $v_A'_x$, and $v_A'_y$ in terms of u (the velocity with which each observer throws his ball) and V (the relative velocity between the coordinate systems). Referring back to equations 7–11 of Chapter VII, we recall that

$$v_x' = \frac{v_x - V}{1 - \frac{Vv_x}{c^2}} \quad \text{and} \quad v_y' = \frac{v_y\sqrt{1 - V^2/c^2}}{1 - \frac{Vv_x}{c^2}} . \tag{7-11}$$

Therefore, knowing from Figure 8.1 that $v_{Ax} = 0$, $v_{Ay} = -u$, $v_B'_x = 0$, $v_B'_y = u$, we have

$$v_A'_x = \frac{v_{Ax} - V}{1 - \frac{Vv_{Ax}}{c^2}} = -V \tag{8-1}$$

$$v_A'_y = \frac{v_{Ay}\sqrt{1 - V^2/c^2}}{1 - \frac{Vv_{Ax}}{c^2}} = -u\sqrt{1 - V^2/c^2} \tag{8-2}$$

$$0 = \frac{v_{Bx} - V}{1 - \frac{Vv_{Bx}}{c^2}} \quad \text{giving} \quad v_{Bx} = V \tag{8-3}$$

and

$$u = \frac{v_{By}\sqrt{1 - V^2/c^2}}{1 - \frac{Vv_{Bx}}{c^2}} \quad \text{giving} \quad v_{By} = u\sqrt{1 - V^2/c^2} . \tag{8-4}$$

The derived values for $v_A'_x$ and v_{Bx} are exactly what we would expect, since the two frames are moving past each other with velocity V. The derived values for $v_A'_y$ and v_{By} differ from the classical value by the factor $\sqrt{1 - V^2/c^2}$. Using these results, we can redraw Figure 8.1, put in the velocity components, and obtain Figure 8.2.

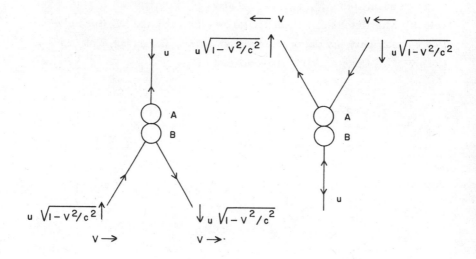

Figure 8.2

Now it will be seen immediately that the classical expression $\vec{p} = m\vec{v}$ won't do for relativistic momentum, because it isn't conserved. The left-hand diagram, for example, has a value of $(\Sigma m v_y)_{before}$ of $-mu + mu\sqrt{1 - v^2/c^2}$ and $(\Sigma m v_y)_{after}$ of $mu - mu\sqrt{1 - v^2/c^2}$, so the y- component of momentum isn't conserved.

How can we find the <u>correct</u> expression for relativistic momentum? If we can think of a reasonable form, it is easy to test it, simply by seeing whether or not it is conserved in our collision process. In an effort to discover such a reasonable form, we pursue the following sequence of arguments:

1. We want to correct the classical momentum $m\vec{v}$ for the effects of relativity. It is reasonable to suppose that this correction is some <u>factor</u> multiplying $m\vec{v}$.

2. We would expect that the factor might depend upon the mass m, velocity $\vec{v}$, and perhaps the speed of light. But the factor must be <u>dimensionless</u>, since $m\vec{v}$ already has the dimensions of momentum. Therefore m cannot enter after all, there being no

other variables to cancel the dimension of mass. The factor can only contain pure numbers, or the ratio $\vec{v}/c$.

3. The factor must be a scalar quantity, since the proper direction of $\vec{p}$ is already accounted for in $m\vec{v}$. So only the magnitude of $\vec{v}$ can enter. We are therefore led to try a relativistic momentum having the form

$$\vec{p} = m\, f\left(\tfrac{v}{c}\right) \vec{v}, \tag{8-5}$$

where $f(v/c)$ is some unknown function of v/c. We demand that $f(0) = 1$, so that our new expression will reduce to the old one for low velocities.

4. Returning to the left-hand diagram of Figure 8.2 (the collision as seen by A), the magnitude of A's velocity is seen to be

$$v^A = \sqrt{v_x^2 + v_y^2} = \sqrt{0 + (-u)^2} = u \tag{8-6}$$

and similarly the magnitude of B's velocity is

$$v^B = \sqrt{v_x^2 + v_y^2} = \sqrt{v^2 + u^2 (1 - v^2/c^2)}. \tag{8-7}$$

We can conserve momentum by requiring that the y-component of the momentum of the two balls be equal and opposite, resulting in no momentum in the y-direction either before or after the collision. Making use of (8-5), (8-6), and (8-7), this condition gives

$$m\, f\left(\tfrac{u}{c}\right) u = m\, f\left(\tfrac{1}{c}\sqrt{v^2 + u^2(1 - v^2/c^2)}\right) u \sqrt{1 - v^2/c^2}. \tag{8-8}$$

Dividing through by $m\, u \sqrt{1 - v^2/c^2}$, we get

$$f\left(\tfrac{1}{c}\sqrt{v^2 + u^2(1 - v^2/c^2)}\right) = \frac{f\left(\tfrac{u}{c}\right)}{\sqrt{1 - v^2/c^2}} \tag{8-9}$$

5. This result must be correct for all velocities, so take in particular $u = 0$. Then (since $f(0) = 1$)

$$f\left(\frac{V}{c}\right) = \frac{1}{\sqrt{1 - V^2/c^2}} \; . \qquad\qquad (8\text{-}10)$$

This is the form our factor takes in a particular case. Let us try this same form for arbitrary velocities. That is, we are led to try the formula

$$\vec{p} = \frac{m\vec{v}}{\sqrt{1 - v^2/c^2}} \; . \qquad\qquad (8\text{-}11)$$

for relativistic momentum, and must now test it in our collision problem. We first evaluate the denominators $\sqrt{1 - v^2/c^2}$ for each ball, using equations (8-6) and (8-7). For ball A, $\sqrt{1 - v^2/c^2} = \sqrt{1 - u^2/c^2}$, and for ball B,

$$\sqrt{1 - v^2/c^2} = \sqrt{1 - \frac{1}{c^2}\left[V^2 + u^2(1 - V^2/c^2)\right]} = \sqrt{1 - V^2/c^2}\sqrt{1 - u^2/c^2}.$$

The y-component of A's momentum before the collision is therefore $p_y{}^A = \dfrac{m(-u)}{\sqrt{1 - u^2/c^2}}$, and the y-component of B's momentum is

$$p_y{}^B = \frac{m\,u\sqrt{1 - V^2/c^2}}{\sqrt{1 - V^2/c^2}\sqrt{1 - u^2/c^2}} = \frac{m\,u}{\sqrt{1 - u^2/c^2}} \; .$$

The total y-component of momentum before the collision is therefore $p_y = p_y{}^A + p_y{}^B = 0$. After the collision, each momentum changes sign, so the sum is still zero. Therefore momentum is indeed conserved if the expression

$$\boxed{\; \vec{p} = \frac{m\,\vec{v}}{\sqrt{1 - v^2/c^2}} \;} \qquad\qquad (8\text{-}12)$$

is used for relativistic momentum.

The relativistic momentum reduces to the classical form $\vec{p} = m\vec{v}$ for velocities much lower than that of light. Also it has the interesting property that the momentum of a particle becomes indefinitely large as $v \to c$. If the classical form $m\vec{v}$ were correct, the momentum couldn't exceed $p = mc$. But in fact, the expression we have found

shows that the momentum of a particle is unbounded, and that a very
small change in the velocity of a highly relativistic particle corresponds to a very large change in its momentum.

The mass m in the equation is the ordinary rest-mass of the particle,
which we can find by weighing it on a scale while it is at rest in our
frame of reference. It is just a constant number for any given object,
and does not depend on velocity. It is common to define a relativistic
mass m_R, which increases with velocity, according to the rule

$$m_R = \frac{m}{\sqrt{1 - v^2/c^2}} \qquad (8\text{-}13)$$

where m is our ordinary rest-mass. Then the relativistic momentum
can be written $\vec{p} = m_R \vec{v}$, which has the classical form. The use of such
a velocity-dependent mass is a matter of taste, to be decided on the
basis of convenience. All equations are actually the same whether one
uses rest-mass or relativistic mass, but they look different by the factor $\sqrt{1 - v^2/c^2}$, due to the definition (8-13). We won't use the idea of a
velocity-dependent relativistic mass any more except in Appendix B,
where we'll discuss various reasons for preferring one over the other.
So it should be remembered that in this book any m in an equation is
just a constant quantity which corresponds to what one would measure
by weighing the object while it is at rest.

As an example of calculating momenta, suppose a muon is created in
the upper atmosphere by cosmic rays, and descends toward the ground
at an angle of 30° from the vertical as seen by a ground observer. If
the meson's total velocity is $v = \frac{4}{5} c$, then the x and y components of
velocity are

$$v_x = v \sin 30° = .4 \, c = 1.2 \times 10^8 \text{ meters/sec}$$

and

$$v_y = v \cos 30° = .4\sqrt{3}\, c = 2.08 \times 10^8 \text{ meters/sec}$$

as shown in Figure 8.3.

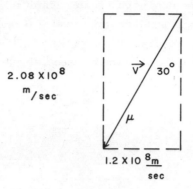

2.08 X 10^8 ^{m}/sec

1.2 X 10 ^{8}$\underline{m}$
sec

Figure 8.3

Using the known muon mass of 1.88×10^{-28} kilograms, we get

$$p_x = \frac{mv_x}{\sqrt{1 - v^2/c^2}} = \frac{(1.88 \times 10^{-28})\,(1.2 \times 10^8)}{\sqrt{1 - (4/5)^2}} = 3.76 \times 10^{-20}\,\frac{\text{kgm-m}}{\text{sec}}\,.$$

and

$$p_y = \frac{mv_y}{\sqrt{1 - v^2/c^2}} = \frac{(1.88 \times 10^{-28})\,(2.08 \times 10^8)}{\sqrt{1 - (4/5)^2}} = 6.53 \times 10^{-20}\,\frac{\text{kgm-m}}{\text{sec}}\,.$$

The total momentum is then $p = \sqrt{p_x{}^2 + p_y{}^2}$ which can equally well be calculated from

$$p = \frac{mv}{\sqrt{1 - v^2/c^2}} = \frac{(1.88 \times 10^{-28})\,(4/5c)}{\sqrt{1 - (4/5)^2}} = 7.52 \times 10^{-20}\,\frac{\text{kgm-m}}{\text{sec}}\,.$$

Thus we have found out what momentum is like in relativity, and can now proceed to investigate relativistic energy.

PROBLEMS VIII

1. A spaceship of mass 10^6 kilograms is coasting through space when it suddenly becomes necessary to accelerate. 1000 kilograms of fuel are forcibly ejected, almost instantaneously, at a speed of $c/2$. How fast will the rocket then be moving compared with its initial velocity?

2. A photon of momentum P_γ strikes a nucleus at rest, and is absorbed. If the mass of the final (excited) nucleus is M, calculate its velocity.

3. Two particles make a head-on collision, stick together and stop dead. The first particle had mass m and speed $3/5$ c, and the second had mass M and speed $4/5$ c. Find M in terms of m.

4. Find the momentum of a distant galaxy moving at $v = c/2$, and having 10^{11} stars of average mass 2×10^{30} kilograms, which is the mass of the sun. How fast would a single proton (mass 1.67×10^{-27} kilograms) have to go to have the same momentum?

CHAPTER IX

RELATIVISTIC ENERGY

THE MOST WIDELY KNOWN and spectacular prediction of special relativity is that mass is a form of energy. Under certain very restrictive circumstances, mass-energy can be converted into kinetic energy on a large scale. In this chapter we'll derive the relativistic expressions for energy, show how the mass-energy $E = mc^2$ comes about, and discuss some applications.

In deriving the expression for relativistic momentum in Chapter VIII, we made use of a perfectly <u>elastic</u> collision. The collision was <u>elastic</u> because we assumed that velocities were the same in magnitude before and after, so that no kinetic energy was lost. Now let us analyze an <u>inelastic</u> process, in which by definition the kinetic energy of motion is <u>not</u> conserved. In particular, consider a mass M which breaks up into two identical pieces, each of mass m. (By now we don't trust any classical "laws of nature," so we're not going to assume that M = 2m!) This break-up process actually occurs in nature. For example, a particle called the K^o-meson decays spontaneously (in about 10^{-10} seconds) into two identical pi-mesons; i.e., $K^o \rightarrow \pi^o + \pi^o$.

Let us view this decay in two coordinate systems, S and S', as shown in Figure 9.1. The initial particle M is at rest in the S frame, and then decays into two particles of mass m, going with equal and opposite

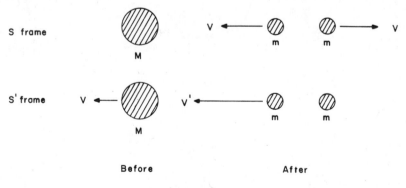

Figure 9.1

velocities v. The momenta, and therefore the velocities, must be
equal and opposite according to conservation of momentum. The S'
frame is moving to the right with velocity v with respect to the S
frame, so that the initial particle moves to the left with velocity v, and
the right-hand final particle is stationary.

First of all, the velocity v' of the left-hand final particle in S' can
be calculated by using the velocity transformation (7-11) of Chapter VII.
We get

$$v' = \frac{(-v) - v}{1 - \frac{(-v)\,v}{c^2}} = \frac{-2v}{1 + v^2/c^2} \ . \tag{9-1}$$

Momentum is obviously conserved in the S-frame. We must also require
it to be conserved in the S' frame. That is,

momentum before = momentum after

$$\frac{M\,(-v)}{\sqrt{1 - v^2/c^2}} = \frac{mv'}{\sqrt{1 - (v')^2/c^2}} + 0 \tag{9-2}$$

and by using the expression for v',

$$\frac{Mv}{\sqrt{1 - v^2/c^2}} = \frac{m2v/(1 + v^2/c^2)}{\{1 - \frac{1}{c^2}\,4v^2/(1 + v^2/c^2)^2\}^{\frac{1}{2}}} = \frac{2mv}{1 - v^2/c^2} \tag{9-3}$$

after some simple algebra.

Solving for M, we have

$$M = \frac{2m}{\sqrt{1 - v^2/c^2}} \tag{9-4}$$

so that the final mass (2m) is less than the initial mass! Mass has been lost
in the process! Now of course something else has increased, namely the
kinetic energy. Obviously the kinetic energy has increased, as one can see
by looking at the decay in frame S, where there is none at all initially.

This kind of situation is what prompted Einstein to conclude that mass
is another form of energy — and in this particle decay we have an example

of the conversion of mass into kinetic energy. If the experiment had been run backwards, with two particles smashing together, we could have created a single particle, and changed the initial kinetic energy into mass.

What remains is to discover how much energy is in a mass m. We expect the mass-energy to be directly proportional to the mass itself, since it is reasonable that doubling the amount of some material will also double its mass-energy. Furthermore, the energy should depend only on the mass, and not (say) on the shape of the mass. Therefore we expect that the mass energy can be written E_m = constant x m. In order to make the dimensions the same on both sides of this equation, the constant must have dimensions of velocity squared. The obvious candidate for such a constant is c^2, or some dimensionless number times c^2, giving a mass-energy E_m = number x mc^2. However, dimensional arguments alone cannot specify the coefficient.

What we need is a straightforward way of finding the mass-energy by using the conservation of energy. Let us suppose only that E_m is given by some unknown function E_m = f(m). Then by requiring that energy be conserved in the decay process, we have (in the S-frame)

$$f(M) = 2f(m) + 2(K. E. \text{ of each final particle}). \qquad (9-5)$$

That is, beforehand all the energy is contained in the original particle M, but afterward some energy is in the masses of the final particles, and some is in their kinetic energy. We don't yet know a relativistic expression for kinetic energy either, but we should require it to approach the classical value K. E. $= \frac{1}{2}mv^2$ for low velocities v.

By conserving momentum in the decay, we have already found that $M = \dfrac{2m}{\sqrt{1 - v^2/c^2}}$, so we can now write

$$f\left(\dfrac{2m}{\sqrt{1 + v^2/c^2}}\right) = 2f(m) + 2(K. E.) . \qquad (9-6)$$

For particular initial and final particles, the velocity v will be perfectly definite. But the equation we have just written should hold for any decay of this type, as long as $M \overset{\geq}{=} 2m$, so that the velocity of each final particle is greater than or equal to zero. Therefore as a special case we can take the limit of the equation as $v \to 0$, so that there is no final kinetic energy. This gives $f(2m) = 2f(m)$, indicating that $f(m)$ is a linear homogeneous function of m, so can be written $f(m) = km$, where k is some constant. In general we would then have

$$\frac{2km}{\sqrt{1 - v^2/c^2}} = 2km + 2\,(K.\,E.)\,. \tag{9-7}$$

We know that $K.\,E. = \frac{1}{2}mv^2$ for small velocities, so let us write equation (9-7) to first order in v^2/c^2. The left-hand side is easily expanded binomially to give

$$2km\,(1 - v^2/c^2)^{-\frac{1}{2}} = 2km\,\{1 - \frac{1}{2}\,(-v^2/c^2) + (-\frac{1}{2})\,(-\frac{3}{2})\,(\frac{1}{2!})\,(\frac{-v^2}{c^2})^2 + \cdots\} \tag{9-8}$$

$$= 2km + 2km\,\frac{1}{2}\frac{v^2}{c^2}$$

to terms of first order in v^2/c^2. To this accuracy

$$2km + 2km \cdot \frac{1}{2}\frac{v^2}{c^2} = 2km + 2\,(K.\,E.)$$

$$= 2km + 2(\frac{1}{2}mv^2) \tag{9-9}$$

from which we immediately obtain $k = c^2$, so the mass-energy of a particle of mass m is

$$\boxed{E_m = mc^2\,.} \tag{9-10}$$

Now returning to the energy conservation equation (9-7) for arbitrary velocities, we find that the relativistic kinetic energy of a particle must be

$$\boxed{K.\,E. = mc^2\left[\frac{1}{\sqrt{1 - v^2/c^2}} - 1\right]} \tag{9-11}$$

85

which has already been shown to reduce to $\frac{1}{2}mv^2$ for small velocities. It then follows that the total energy (mass-energy + kinetic energy) of a particle is

$$E = \frac{mc^2}{\sqrt{1 - v^2/c^2}} . \qquad (9\text{-}12)$$

These expressions were derived by conserving energy in the rest-frame of the initial particle. The reader can check them by showing that energy is conserved in the S' frame also. Note carefully that $E = mc^2$ + K. E. is the total energy of an object, including the mass-energy, and that the kinetic energy is not $\frac{1}{2}mv^2$, except in the limit of small velocities.

It is interesting to note the simple and useful relation between energy and momentum

$$E^2 = p^2c^2 + m^2c^4 \qquad (9\text{-}13)$$

which follows directly from the definitions of E and p. This relation is extremely useful in analyzing particle collisions and decays, which are taken up in Chapter XI. The form of the equation is particularly interesting when we discuss spacetime in Chapter XIII.

The analysis of energy in relativity provides further insight into why objects cannot go as fast as the velocity of light. The kinetic energy

$$mc^2 \left[\frac{1}{\sqrt{1 - v^2/c^2}} - 1 \right] \qquad (9\text{-}11)$$

becomes infinite as $v \rightarrow c$. In other words, for very high velocities the energy in the object can be greatly increased without changing the velocity much at all.

We should emphasize here the difference between the classical and relativistic views of mass and energy. Before Einstein, it was thought that mass and energy were separately conserved. No matter what a collection of particles were doing, whether colliding, combining, exploding, or whatever, their total mass always remained the same. Similarly,

86

for a closed system with no applied external forces and no escape of energy, energy was conserved.. Now we have seen that in relativistic physics mass is <u>not</u> conserved, so one classical conservation law has been proved false. But if mass-energy is included, the total <u>energy</u> of a system is still conserved. Two classical conservation laws have been merged by the theory of relativity into a single law, the conservation of "mass and energy."

As an example illustrating the difference between classical and relativistic energy, suppose a couple of wooden blocks of mass m are held together by a string opposing the outward force of a compressed spring placed between them, as in Figure 9.2.

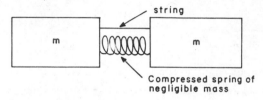

Figure 9.2

According to classical mechanics, the total mass of the system is 2m, and the potential energy is

$$U = \frac{1}{2} k \, (\Delta x)^2 \tag{9-14}$$

where k is the force-constant of the spring, and Δx is the compressed distance. If now the string is cut, the blocks will fly apart, as shown in Figure 9.3.

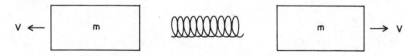

Figure 9.3

Still according to classical mechanics, the final mass is 2m by mass conservation, and the final kinetic energy is

$$2 \left(\frac{1}{2} m v^2 \right) = \frac{1}{2} k \, (\Delta x)^2 \tag{9-15}$$

87

by energy conservation. We've used the fact that the velocities of the two blocks are equal and opposite, due to conservation of momentum. The velocity of each block is therefore

$$v = \sqrt{\frac{k}{2m}} \ \Delta x. \tag{9-16}$$

How is this experiment to be described by <u>relativistic</u> mechanics? Actually we have already shown how to do it at the beginning of this chapter. If the mass of each block is m when it is weighed <u>by itself</u>, then the mass of the combination when the spring is compressed will be <u>greater</u> than 2m, as shown in equation (9-4). If the mass of the combination is M, which we can find in principle by weighing it, then the final velocity of each block will be the solution of $M = \dfrac{2m}{\sqrt{1 - v^2/c^2}}$ or

$$v = c \sqrt{1 - 4 \ m^2/M^2} \ . \tag{9-17}$$

The relativistic approach to finding the final velocity is impractical in this case, because it is much easier to use the classical method of measuring the force constant and compression of the spring than to weigh the combination accurately enough to tell the difference between M and 2m. For example, suppose each block has a velocity of 3 meters/sec after the string is cut. Then the mass of the initial combination must have been

$$M = \frac{2m}{\sqrt{1 - v^2/c^2}} = \frac{2m}{\sqrt{1 - (3/3 \times 10^8)^2}} = \frac{2m}{\sqrt{1 - 10^{-16}}}$$

$$\cong 2m \ (1 + \frac{1}{2} \times 10^{-16}) \tag{9-18}$$

which would be very difficult to tell apart from 2m. But in nuclear or elementary particle physics, the relativistic approach is the <u>only</u> possibility. In the K^o-meson decay

$$K^o \rightarrow \pi^o + \pi^o$$

there isn't any spring whose force-constant and compression can be measured. Also the mass lost in the decay is a substantial fraction of the total, so the pions move with relativistic velocities. The mass of

88

a K^0-meson is 8.85×10^{-28} kgm, and the mass of each pion is 2.4×10^{-28} kgm, so formula 9-17 says that each pion will be moving at speed $v = .84$ c!

In the example of the two blocks, there was a repulsive force which tended to separate them. This caused a positive "interaction energy" which made the combination slightly heavier than the two blocks weighed individually. Conversely, if a number of particles are attracted to each other, the combination will have a mass which is less than the sum of the individual particle masses. This is easy to see by conservation of energy. Since the particles are trying to stick together, energy must be added to rip them apart. The energy will show up in a greater total mass-energy after the combination is split up. Thus a hydrogen atom weighs a little less than the weight of a proton plus the weight of an electron. Similarly, an atomic nucleus weighs less than the combined weights of the protons and neutrons weighed separately.

Since the main use of relativity is in atomic and nuclear physics, we will quit using kilograms and joules as units of mass and energy. The unit most often used for such things is the electron volt, which is the kinetic energy gained by an electron accelerating through an electrical potential of one volt. It is related to the joule by

$$1 \text{ electron volt} = 1.60 \times 10^{-19} \text{ joules.} \qquad (9\text{-}19)$$

The electron volt, or "ev," is a convenient unit for atomic physics: for example, the binding energy of a hydrogen atom is about 13.6 ev. That is, 13.6 ev have to be supplied to the atom in order to rip the electron and proton apart. The binding energy of the "deuteron" (the nucleus of deuterium or heavy hydrogen) is about 2.2 million electron volts ("Mev"), meaning that 2.2 Mev is required to separate the neutron and proton.

Instead of inventing a small unit for mass as well, we can express the mass of particles in terms of their mass-energy, which can be written in Mev units. For example, the mass-energy of an electron is .511 Mev, meaning that $m_e c^2 = .511$ Mev. Similarly, the mass-energies of the neutron and proton are 938.2 and 936.5 Mev, respectively. So the

89

mass-energy of the deuteron is 938.2 + 936.5 - 2.2 = 1872.5 Mev by subtracting the binding energy, as just explained.

The expressions we've found for momentum and total energy can be written

$$\vec{p} = \gamma m \vec{v} \quad \text{and} \quad E = \gamma mc^2 \quad \text{where } \gamma = \frac{1}{\sqrt{1 - v^2/c^2}}. \tag{9-20}$$

So if the mass and velocity of a particle are known, the momentum and energy can be easily calculated. The equations are also useful in the forms

$$\gamma = \frac{E}{mc^2} \tag{9-21}$$

which gives the γ-factor (and therefore the velocity) in terms of known mass and total energy, and

$$\vec{v} = \frac{\gamma m \vec{v}}{\gamma m} = \frac{\vec{p}c^2}{E} \tag{9-22}$$

giving the particle velocity immediately from the momentum and total energy.

As an example, consider electrons in a 1.5 billion electron volt (Bev) electron synchrotron. Their total energy is about 3000 times their mass-energy ($m_e c^2$ = .511 Mev), so $\gamma = 3000 = \frac{1}{\sqrt{1 - v^2/c^2}}$ from which we get v = .999999945c! The momentum of these electrons is $p = \frac{mv}{\sqrt{1 - v^2/c^2}}$ = 3000 mv $\cong$ 3000 mc, which is 3000 times as large as you would expect for this velocity by classical mechanics.

Since the Mev unit is so convenient in nuclear and elementary particle physics, it is common to express energies in Mev units, momenta in Mev/c units, and mass in Mev/c^2 units. From the equation

$$E^2 = p^2c^2 + m^2c^4 \tag{9-13}$$

relating these three quantities, it is clear that mc^2 and pc have dimensions of energy, so it is possible to measure mass as so many "Mev/c^2," and momentum as so many "Mev/c." As an example of using these units and the relativistic equations for momentum and energy, we will return to the $K^O \rightarrow \pi^O + \pi^O$ decay mentioned at the beginning of the chapter. Given the masses of all particles and the reference frame in which the experiment is viewed, we can calculate the energy, momentum, and velocity of the decay pions.

The mass of a K^O-meson is 498 Mev/c^2, and the mass of each pion is 135 Mev/c^2. In the "center-of-mass" frame, in which the initial K^O-meson is at rest, conservation of momentum requires that the π^O's emerge with equal and opposite momenta, as shown in Figure 9.4. Therefore the speeds and kinetic energies of the two pions are equal also. Since the initial energy is entirely in the mass of the K^O, energy conservation requires that

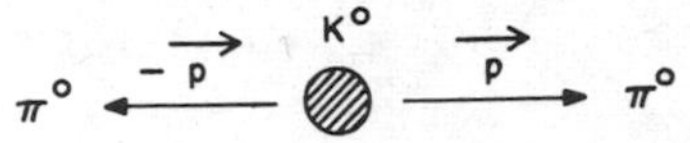

Figure 9.4

$$M_K c^2 = E_\pi$$

so the total energy of each π^O is

$$E_\pi = \frac{M_K c^2}{2} = \frac{498}{2} \text{ Mev} = 249 \text{ Mev.}$$

Because the total energy is the sum of the mass-energy and kinetic energy, the kinetic energy of each π^O is

$$K.E. = E_\pi - M_\pi c^2 = 249 \text{ Mev} - 135 \text{ Mev} = 114 \text{ Mev.}$$

By the relation $E^2 = p^2 c^2 + m^2 c^4$, the momentum of each π^O is

$$p_\pi = \frac{1}{c} \sqrt{E_\pi^2 - M_\pi^2 c^4} = 210 \text{ Mev/c}$$

and the velocity of each π^O is

$$v_\pi = \frac{p_\pi c^2}{E_\pi} = \frac{210 \text{ Mev c}}{249 \text{ Mev}} = .845 \text{ c.}$$

Relativity is not only needed to understand elementary particles for their own sake, but must also be used to understand some very important large scale phenomena. For example, the energy of stars comes from converting mass-energy into kinetic energy through nuclear fusion reactions. This kinetic energy is of course just <u>heat</u> when looked at on a large scale. Most stars use the conversion of hydrogen into helium (called hydrogen burning) as their principle source of energy, although stars in an advanced stage of evolution may burn heavier elements instead. Our sun runs <u>mainly</u> on the proton-proton chain, which begins with the collision of two protons to form a deuteron, a positron (an anti-electron), and a neutrino:[*]

$$p + p \rightarrow d + e^+ + \nu.$$

Then the deuteron may be hit by another proton to form the isotope He^3, which consists of two protons and one neutron:

$$d + p \rightarrow He^3 + \gamma\text{'s}$$

where one or more photons (γ's)[**] may be created as well. Finally, two He^3 nuclei may collide, and end up as a He^4 nucleus (2 protons + 2 neutrons) and two protons:[***]

$$He^3 + He^3 \rightarrow He^4 + p + p.$$

Mass is turned into kinetic energy at each stage of this "chain," so the star is kept hot. When all the hydrogen is used up, the star undergoes a fairly rapid change, becoming smaller and hotter, and begins to burn helium into carbon and heavier nuclei. Our sun is supposed to reach this stage in about four or five billion years.

---

[*] Particles are described and discussed in Chapters X and XI and in Appendix I.

[**] Photons are described in Chapter X.

[***] This final reaction converting He^3 into He^4 can occur in other ways, as shown in reference 2.

REFERENCES

1. The relativistic relationship between speed and kinetic energy has been very cleanly demonstrated experimentally, as reported in an article "Speed and Kinetic Energy of Relativistic Electrons," by W. Bertozzi, in the American Journal of Physics 32, 551 (1964).

2. There are many articles on energy production in the stars. A non-mathematical review is contained in an article entitled "Nuclear Astrophysics" by A. G. W. Cameron in the Annual Review of Nuclear Science, Vol. 8, 1958. The standard technical paper by Burbidge, Burbidge, Fowler, and Hoyle is in the Reviews of Modern Physics 29, p. 547 (1957).

3. Einstein discusses energy in his original article referred to in Chapter III, and also in the article "Does the Inertia of a Body Depend Upon its Energy-Content?" translated in The Principle of Relativity (Dover Publications 1923). He also discusses it in his books listed in the main bibliography.

PROBLEMS IX

1. The total energy of a particular proton emitted by the Brookhaven synchrotron is 30 Bev. The mass-energy of a proton is 936 Mev. Find its kinetic energy, momentum, and velocity.

2. A free neutron at rest decays in about 15 minutes into a proton, electron, and antineutrino. The mass-energies of these particles are: neutron, 938.2 Mev; proton, 936.5 Mev; electron, .511 Mev; antineutrino, zero. Find the total kinetic energy of the decay products.

3. Calculate the work-energy required to accelerate a 10^6 kilogram spaceship to a speed such that from our frame of reference the spaceman inside ages only 1/10 as fast as we do. Compare this energy with the mass-energy of the ship.

4. Does an average proton or electron at 15 million degrees Kelvin (about the temperature at the center of the sun) have to be treated

by relativistic mechanics? (The average kinetic energy of a particle is $\frac{3}{2}$ kT, where k is Boltzmann's constant.)

5. A U^{238} nucleus decays in about 4.5×10^8 years into an α particle (He^4 nucleus) and the Th^{234} nucleus. In atomic mass units (amu), defined by 1 amu = 931.49 Mev/c^2 (corresponding to M_{carbon} = 12.0000 amu) the masses are U^{238}:238.0508 and α particle: 4.0026. The emerging α-particle has a kinetic energy of 4.19 Mev.

    a.   Assuming the Th^{234} nucleus takes away negligible kinetic energy, calculate its mass.

    b.   Justify the assumption by calculating the kinetic energy of the Th^{234} nucleus by using momentum conservation.

    c.   Is the α-particle moving fast enough to be treated relativistically?

CHAPTER X
LIGHT AND MASSLESS PARTICLES

THE PRECEDING chapters have discussed the energy and momentum of objects having mass. But so far, not much has been said about light. In this chapter we will investigate the energy and momentum of light, and also discuss various massless particles and their properties.

A. Light Energy and Momentum

Everyone knows that light carries energy as it travels; it is also true that light carries momentum. The momentum carried in a beam of light causes the phenomenon of radiation-pressure, which is small in most laboratory situations. When a light beam strikes a surface, momentum will be transferred to the surface, so we say that light carries momentum. Under extreme conditions, where the light intensity is huge, radiation pressure can become very important. In fact, some particularly hot stars are largely supported against collapse by the pressure of the radiation pushing out through them.

It is found experimentally that a parallel beam of light having energy E carries a momentum p given by $p = E/c$. The higher the energy in the beam, the greater momentum it has. This relation is also predicted theoretically by the electromagnetic wave theory of light. Knowing the momentum of light, and using conservation of momentum, we can think of experiments to do with light and ordinary masses. For example, suppose a man with a flashlight is set out by himself in empty space. He points the flashlight away from him and turns it quickly on and off, thereby emitting a short pulse of light of energy E, as shown in Figure 10-1. Because the light carries some momentum, the man will recoil, drifting slowly in a direction opposite to that of the light beam. Since he moves so slowly (the momentum of light from a flashlight is extremely small), his momentum is just the classical value $p = mv$. Conserving momentum, we must have $mv = P_{light} = \dfrac{E}{c}$, because there was no momentum at the beginning. The man's velocity is therefore $v = E/mc$, where m is his mass.

$v = E/mc$

c

Figure 10.1

Now notice that the center of mass of the system is moving! The
light carries no mass, so the center-of-mass is fixed on the man.
Classically, we know that if no external forces are applied to a system,
its center of mass should not accelerate. This "law" has therefore
been violated, which should not be surprising, since mass itself is
frequently not conserved. However, energy as a whole certainly is
conserved, so perhaps we can show that the relativistically correct
theorem is that if there are no external forces, the "center of energy"
remains fixed. Then the energy E of the light could "balance" the energy of the man, which is essentially his mass-energy mc^2, since his
kinetic energy is negligible by comparison.

In order to balance energy, we must have

$$m_{man} c^2 \times \text{(distance man moves)} = E_{light} \times \text{(distance light moves)}.$$
$$(10\text{-}1)$$

In time t, the man moves a distance $vt = \dfrac{E}{mc} t$, and the light moves a
distance ct. Therefore, for equilibrium

$$m c^2 \cdot \frac{E}{mc} t = E ct,$$
$$(10\text{-}2)$$

which is an identity, verifying the "center-of-energy" theorem. Without much trouble, the reader will be able to show that our assumption
that the man moves slowly is not necessary, as suggested in problem
10-1. Even if his flashlight emits such a powerful burst of γ-rays that
he attains relativistic velocities, the center-of-energy theorem is
correct.

We have shown that the requirement of zero total momentum is equivalent to the requirement that the center-of-energy remain at rest. Even though it is center-of-energy which is meant, it is common even in relativistic problems to speak of "center-of-mass" since everyone is so used to it from classical mechanics. In fact if we define an "effective mass"

$$m_{eff} = E/c^2 \qquad (10\text{-}3)$$

for any kind of energy E, including kinetic energy, the center of mass does remain fixed in relativity, if effective masses are included. In the flashlight experiment, we would assign to the light pulse an effective mass of E/c^2 where E is the energy of the pulse. It is often useful in relativistic problems involving particle collisions and decays to use the center-of-mass frame, which should be taken to mean the reference frame in which the total momentum of the system is zero.

B. Massless Particles

In the first few years of the twentieth century, it was discovered that some experiments involving light could be explained only by thinking of light as being composed of particles, called photons. Such phenomena as black-body radiation, the photoelectric effect,[*] and (somewhat later) Compton scattering,[**] showed the energy of a photon in the light-beam of frequency ν is given by

$$E = h\nu \qquad (10\text{-}4)$$

where the proportionality constant h, called Planck's constant, is $h = 6.627 \times 10^{-34}$ joule-seconds. Thus a high-frequency gamma-ray photon emitted from an atomic nucleus has more energy than a low-frequency radio-wave photon emitted from an accelerating electron in an antenna. If a monochromatic beam of light has frequency ν and

---

[*] A. Einstein, Annalen der Physik 17, 132 (1905 — The same year he published on special relativity!).

[**] See page 106.

total energy E, then $E = nh\nu$, where n is the number of photons in the beam.

Since the photons move at the speed of light, it is clear from the equations

$$\vec{p} = \frac{m\vec{v}}{\sqrt{1 - v^2/c^2}} \quad \text{and} \quad E = \frac{m c^2}{\sqrt{1 - v^2/c^2}} \qquad \text{(8-12) and (9-12)}$$

that photons must also be <u>massless</u>, since otherwise they would have infinite momentum and energy. Therefore these equations are of no help in computing the momentum or energy of photons. However, the relation $E^2 = p^2 c^2 + m^2 c^4$ <u>is</u> correct for photons, if we take $m = 0$, since it reduces to $E = p c$, which has been experimentally verified for individual photons as well as for light-beams as a whole. Therefore the momentum of a photon can be written $p = \frac{E}{c} = \frac{h\nu}{c}$. Photons are never slowed down or stopped: they move at speed c from the moment they are created to the moment they are destroyed.

Aside from photons, there are other massless particles called <u>neutrinos</u>. They must also move at speed c in order to carry energy and momentum. Denoted by the symbol ν,[*] they show up in the decay of unstable particles or in the β-decay of radioactive nuclei. Neutrinos were postulated by W. Pauli in 1931, in order to understand an apparent violation of the conservation laws of energy, momentum, and angular momentum. They are so hard to detect that they weren't discovered directly until 1956, when they were observed in the reaction

$$\bar{\nu} + p \rightarrow n + e^+$$

in which an incoming antineutrino converts a target proton into a neutron and a positron.

Photons and neutrinos are similar in that they are massless, move at the speed of light, and have no electric charge. They differ in their spin angular momentum: A photon has spin <u>one</u> (in units of $h/2\pi$, where

---

[*] not to be confused with the frequency of light!

h is again Planck's constant) and a neutrino has spin <u>one-half</u>. They also differ in the manner and strength with which they interact with other particles. But we have discussed them here because they are especially distinguished by being the most relativistic of particles.

REFERENCES

1. The influence of radiation pressure on the structure of stars is discussed in many books on astrophysics, such as <u>Structure and Evolution of the Stars</u> by M. Schwarzchild (Princeton University Press, 1958).

2. The relation $E = pc$ for light is derived from electromagnetic theory in almost any advanced textbook on electromagnetism.

3. The inertia of light waves is treated by Einstein in his article "Does the Inertia of a Body Depend Upon Its Energy Content?" translated in <u>The Principle of Relativity</u> (Dover Publications, 1923).

PROBLEMS X

1. In the experiment with a man and a flashlight, show that the center of energy remains at rest even if the man attains a relativistic velocity.

2. A γ-ray photon emitted from an excited Li^7 nucleus has an energy of .478 Mev. Calculate its momentum in units of Mev/c, and its frequency in seconds^{-1}.

3. An electron-positron pair at rest disintegrates into two photons of equal energy: e^+ and $e^- \rightarrow \gamma + \gamma$. Find the wavelength of each photon.

4. An anti-neutrino $\bar{\nu}$ of momentum 2 Mev/c strikes a proton at rest. Is the reaction

    $$\bar{\nu} + p \rightarrow n + e^+$$

    possible for this neutrino?

CHAPTER XI
PARTICLE COLLISIONS AND DECAYS

MUCH OF WHAT IS KNOWN about nuclear physics, and almost every-thing known about the fundamental particles, has come from looking at collision and decay processes at relativistic energies. Analyzing events like these is the most important application of the expressions for the energy and momentum of relativistic particles. Just as in classical mechanics, the conservation laws are very useful in analyzing the out-come of collisions. If the initial motions of a group of particles are known, the laws of energy and momentum conservation restrict the final motions to those for which the energy and momentum are the same before and after. In fact we have already used the decay process $K^o \rightarrow \pi^o + \pi^o$, assuming momentum and energy conservation, to derive the expression for total energy in Chapter IX. Now that we have it, we can investigate other decays, and also particle collisions.

A. π^o Decay (Decay into two massless particles)

The π^o meson decays in about 10^{-16} seconds into two photons, written $\pi^o \rightarrow 2\gamma$. As in any decay process, it is easier to treat in the rest-frame of the initial particle, which is also the center-of-mass frame. Conservation of energy requires that

Energy before = Energy after

$$E_\pi = m_\pi c^2 = E_{\gamma_1} + E_{\gamma_2} \tag{11-1}$$

where we've used the fact that all of the pion's energy is mass-energy, since it isn't moving. Momentum conservation says that

momentum before = momentum after

$$0 = \vec{P}_{\gamma_1} + \vec{P}_{\gamma_2} \tag{11-2}$$

which tells us immediately that the two photons come off with equal and opposite momenta, as shown in Figure 11.1.

Using the energy-momentum relation $E^2 = p^2c^2 + m^2c^4$, which reduces to $E = pc$ for the massless photons, it follows that each

Figure 11.1

photon must have the same energy also. The energy of each photon will be half of the π^0 rest-energy, or 67.5 Mev.

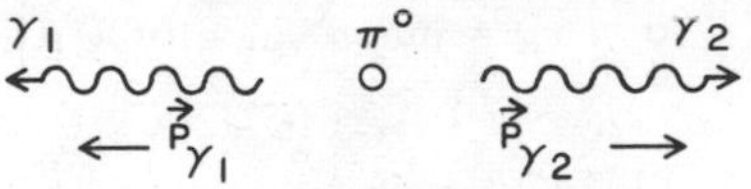

B. $\pi^{\pm}$ Decay (Decay into a massless and a massive particle)

A slightly more complicated decay is that of the π^+ or π^- meson, which decay in about 2.5×10^{-8} seconds into a muon and neutrino, written $\pi^{\pm} \to \mu^{\pm} + \nu$. In the pion rest-frame

$$E_\pi = m_\pi c^2 = E_\mu + E_\nu \text{ (energy conservation)}$$
$$0 = \vec{p}_\mu + \vec{p}_\nu \text{ (momentum conservation)} ,$$

(11-3)

the last equation showing that the muon and neutrino depart with equal and opposite momenta, $\vec{p}_\mu = -\vec{p}_\nu$. Squaring and multiplying by c^2 gives

$$p_\mu^2 c^2 = p_\nu^2 c^2 \quad \text{or} \quad E_\mu^2 - m_\mu^2 c^4 = E_\nu^2$$

(11-4)

where we have used the relation $E_\mu^2 = p_\mu^2 c^2 + m_\mu^2 c^4$ for the muon, and $E_\nu = p_\nu c$ for the neutrino. E_ν can be eliminated by the energy conservation result $E_\nu = m_\pi c^2 - E_\mu$, so

$$E_\mu^2 - m_\mu^2 c^4 = E_\nu^2 = m_\pi^2 c^4 - 2m_\pi c^2 E_\mu + E_\mu^2 ,$$

$$\text{or} \quad E_\mu = \frac{(m_\pi^2 + m_\mu^2) c^2}{2 m_\pi}$$

(11-5)

which gives the muon energy in terms of the known pion and muon masses. Having found E_μ, we can then find

a) $(K.E.)_\mu = E_\mu - m_\mu c^2$

b) $p_\mu = \frac{1}{c}\sqrt{E_\mu^2 - m_\mu^2 c^4}$

(11-6)

c) v_μ = muon velocity = $p_\mu c^2 / E_\mu$

d) $\gamma_\mu = \dfrac{1}{\sqrt{1 - v_\mu^2/c^2}} = \dfrac{E_\mu}{m_\mu c^2}$

(11-6 continued)

e) $|\vec{p}_\nu| = |\vec{p}_\mu|$

f) $E_\nu = p_\nu c$.

C. Λ Decay (Decay into two massive particles)

Another type of decay is illustrated by the Λ-particle, which breaks up in about 10^{-10} seconds into two particles having mass, a proton and a pi-minus meson ($\Lambda \rightarrow p + \pi^-$). There are many decays of this type, including

$\Lambda \rightarrow n + \pi^0$ (an alternative lambda decay mode)

$\Xi^- \rightarrow \Lambda + \pi^-$ (a "cascade-particle" decay)

and the more recently discovered omega-minus decays

$$\Omega^- \rightarrow \Xi^- + \pi^0 \qquad \text{or} \qquad \Omega^- \rightarrow \Xi^0 + \pi^- ,$$

all with lifetimes of about 10^{-10} seconds.

Conserving energy in the Λ-decay,

$$E_\Lambda = M_\Lambda c^2 = E_p + E_\pi \tag{11-7}$$

and conserving momentum,

$$0 = \vec{p}_p + \vec{p}_\pi, \qquad \text{or} \qquad p_p^2 c^2 = p_\pi^2 c^2.$$

Using $E^2 = p^2 c^2 + m^2 c^4$ for each final particle, this last equation can be written $E_p^2 - m_p^2 c^4 = E_\pi^2 - m_\pi^2 c^4$ and then E_p can be eliminated by the energy-conservation formula $E_p = M_\Lambda c^2 - E_\pi$. This gives

$$E_\pi^2 = m_\pi^2 c^4 - m_p^2 c^4 + (M_\Lambda c^2 - E_\pi)^2$$

$$= (m_\pi^2 - m_p^2 + M_\Lambda^2)c^4 - 2M_\Lambda c^2 E_\pi + E_\pi^2$$

or

$$E_\pi = \frac{(M_\Lambda^2 - m_p^2 + m_\pi^2)\,c^2}{2M_\Lambda} \qquad (11\text{-}8)$$

which relates the pion energy to known particle masses. (Alternatively, if the lambda mass were unknown, an experimental measurement of E_π could be used to determine it.) Other variables are easily found:

a) $(K.E.)_\pi = E_\pi - m_\pi c^2$

b) $p_\pi = \dfrac{1}{c}\sqrt{E_\pi^2 - m_\pi^2 c^4}$

c) $v_\pi = p_\pi c^2 / E_\pi$ $\qquad\qquad\qquad (11\text{-}9)$

d) $|\vec{p}_p| = |\vec{p}_\pi|$

e) $E_p = \sqrt{p_p^2 c^2 + m_p^2 c^4} = M_\Lambda c^2 - E_\pi$

and so on.

D. Decay into Three Particles

In the preceding examples, it was seen that the conservation laws are such a powerful restriction that the energy and momentum of each final particle in a two-particle decay is completely determined by the particle masses. Why can't a particle decay into just one other particle? The obvious explanation is that in this case the conservation laws are so restrictive that this kind of decay can't happen at all, except in the case that the initial and final particles have the same mass. That is, the final particle must be at rest in the rest-frame of the initial particle by momentum conservation, so it must have the same mass-energy by energy conservation.*

---

*   In the cases where two different particles have the same mass, they are usually prevented from decaying into one another by other conservation laws, like charge and angular momentum conservation.

There are some particles which do not decay into two particles, but do decay into three. There are others which may do either. The muon, for example, eventually breaks up into an electron, a neutrino, and an anti-neutrino

$$\mu^{\pm} \to e^{\pm} + \nu + \bar{\nu} \qquad (2.2 \times 10^{-6} \text{ seconds})$$

and the free neutron (i.e., a neutron by itself, not bound up inside a nucleus) decays into a proton, an electron, and an anti-neutrino

$$n \to p + e^{-} + \bar{\nu} . \qquad \text{(about 15 minutes)}$$

In these cases, the conservation laws cannot specify the energy or momentum of each final particle — there are a wide range of possibilities. For example, any one of the final particles in the neutron decay could have zero momentum, with the remaining two emerging with equal and opposite momenta, and enough energy to satisfy energy conservation. But if the momentum of one final particle is known, the momentum and energy of each of the other particles can be calculated from the conservation laws.

E. Photoproduction of Pions

The collision of two stable particles is the usual method for producing unstable particles, and is a way of studying the stable particles themselves. Almost always one of the initial particles is essentially at rest, so is called the "target" particle. The "bombarding" particle may have come from cosmic rays or some kind of accelerating machine. As an example of a collision process, consider the production of pi-mesons by bombarding stationary protons with γ-ray photons. We can produce either π^{+} or π^{0} mesons this way, by means of the reactions[*]

$$\gamma + p \to \pi^{0} + p \qquad \text{and} \qquad \gamma + p \to \pi^{+} + n.$$

In the laboratory the target proton is at rest (for example as a hydrogen nucleus in a liquid hydrogen bubble chamber). The first reaction is shown schematically in Figure 11.2.

---

[*] π^{-} mesons can be produced by $\gamma + n \to \pi^{-} + p$.

104

Treating this π^0 photoproduction process, energy conservation gives

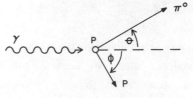

$$E_\gamma + m_p c^2 = E_\pi + E_p.$$

Figure 11.2

Momentum conservation, using the angles defined in Figure 11.2, gives

$\vec{p}_\gamma = \vec{p}_\pi + \vec{p}_p$ which in component form becomes

$$p_\gamma = p_\pi \cos \theta + p_p \cos \phi \quad \text{(in the incident direction)} \qquad (11\text{-}10)$$

$$0 = p_\pi \sin \theta - p_p \sin \phi \quad \text{(in the perpendicular direction)}.$$

Usually we aren't interested in the proton recoil angle ϕ, so we can eliminate it between these two equations for momentum conservation. The easiest way to do this is to draw the "momentum conservation

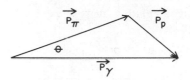

Figure 11.3

triangle" of Figure 11.3, which shows that $\vec{p}_\gamma = \vec{p}_\pi + \vec{p}_p$. By the law of cosines,

$$p_p^2 = p_\pi^2 + p_\gamma^2 - 2 p_\pi p_\gamma \cos \theta \qquad (11\text{-}11)$$

which is the same result obtained by eliminating the angle θ between the momentum component equations. In addition to energy and momentum conservation, we need to make use of the formula $E^2 = p^2 c^2 + m^2 c^4$ for the particles involved. This gives

$$E_\gamma = p_\gamma c, \qquad E_\pi = \sqrt{p_\pi^2 c^2 + m_\pi^2 c^4},$$

$$\text{and } E_p = \sqrt{p_p^2 c^2 + m_p^2 c^4} . \qquad (11\text{-}12)$$

The conservation of energy can then be written

$$p_\gamma c + m_p c^2 = \sqrt{p_\pi^2 c^2 + m_\pi^2 c^4} + \sqrt{p_p^2 c^2 + m_p^2 c^4} \qquad (11\text{-}13)$$

and conservation of momentum implies, as we have seen,

105

$$p_p^{\ 2} = p_\pi^{\ 2} + p_\gamma^{\ 2} - 2\,p_\pi p_\gamma \cos\theta. \qquad (11\text{-}11)$$

These latter two equations serve as a constraint on the momenta of the final particles. We know the particle masses, and we may also know the momentum of the incoming photon. If so, there are three unknowns, p_π, p_p, and $\cos\theta$, and two equations involving them. Therefore these quantities are not determined, but if one unknown is specified, the others can be calculated. For example, an experiment can be set up with the pion detector at some fixed angle θ from the incident photon direction. If a pion is detected at this angle, from the conservation laws we can deduce both its momentum and the momentum of the recoil proton. If our principal interest is in the pion momentum at various angles, the proton momentum p_p can be eliminated between the two equations, resulting in a single relation for $p_\pi = f\,(\cos\theta)$.

F. Compton Scattering

One of the first experiments showing that light has a particle aspect (i.e., should sometimes be thought of as consisting of photons) was performed and analyzed by A. H. Compton in 1922.[*] He fired a beam of x-rays at a block of graphite, and measured the wavelength of the scattered x-rays as a function of the angle at which they emerge. If we assume that electrons in the graphite are causing the scattering, the collision would look as shown in Figure 11.4.

Energy conservation gives

$$h\nu + m_e c^2 = h\nu' + E_e \qquad (11\text{-}14)$$

and the momentum conservation triangle along with the law of cosines gives

$$p_e^{\ 2} = \left(\frac{h\nu}{c}\right)^2 + \left(\frac{h\nu'}{c}\right)^2 - 2\,\frac{h\nu}{c}\,\frac{h\nu'}{c}\cos\theta. \qquad (11\text{-}15)$$

The electron momentum and energy are related by

---

[*] Phys. Rev. 22, 409 (1923).

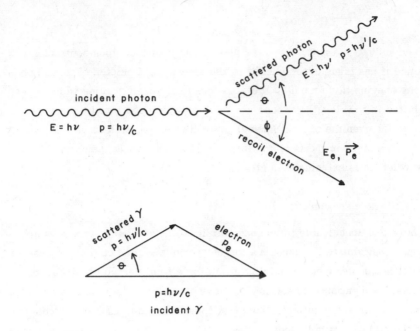

Figure 11.4

$$p_e c^2 = E_e^2 - m_e^2 c^4$$

$$= (h\nu - h\nu' + m_e c^2)^2 - m_e^2 c^4 \qquad (11-16)$$

$$= h^2 (\nu - \nu')^2 + 2h\, m_e c^2 (\nu - \nu')$$

using the energy conservation formula.

Eliminating the electron momentum between this equation and the momentum–conservation equation gives

$$h^2 (\nu - \nu')^2 + 2h\, m_e c^2 (\nu - \nu') = h^2 \nu^2 + h^2 {\nu'}^2 - 2\, h\nu\, h\nu' \cos\theta$$

which can be simplified by cancelling terms to

$$m_e c^2 (\nu - \nu') = h\, \nu\, \nu'\, (1 - \cos\theta). \qquad (11-17)$$

The result can be further simplified by substituting the frequency-wavelength relations $\nu = c/\lambda$ and $\nu' = c/\lambda'$ to get the final Compton scattering formula

$$\lambda' - \lambda = \frac{h}{m_e c}(1 - \cos\theta).\tag{11-18}$$

Obviously $\lambda' > \lambda$ if $\theta > 0$, so the photon has reddened upon scattering, since it has transferred energy to the electron. Compton observed photons obeying this formula. He also found scattered photons which weren't shifted in wavelength. These are photons which scattered off a whole atom (or even the crystal lattice) instead of a single electron. In this case the mass in the Compton formula is so large that the change in wavelength is extremely small.

G. Illegal Reactions

There are conceivable processes which are nevertheless forbidden because they violate the conservation of energy and momentum. A case in point is the decay of a particle into a single final particle of different mass, as mentioned in section D. It is also easy to see that an electron and a positron (an anti-electron) can't annihilate one another, producing in their place a single photon: that is, $e^- + e^+ \not\to \gamma$. This can be proved in any reference frame, but it is most easily verified in the center-of-mass frame, in which by definition there is no net momentum. In this frame the electron and positron move toward each other with equal speeds. By energy conservation, the resulting photon energy would be $E_\gamma = 2E_e$ $= 2\,(m_e c^2 + (\text{K. E.})_e)$, or twice the total energy of each initial particle. But the energy and momentum of a photon are related by $E_\gamma = p_\gamma c$, so the photon momentum is considerable, which contradicts the zero momentum required by momentum conservation. Having proved the reaction can't occur when viewed from the center-of-mass frame, it is evident that it can't occur when viewed from any frame.* In exactly the same way you can show that an electron by itself cannot radiate ($e \not\to e + \gamma$).

Other illegal reactions include those in which a particle decays into two or more particles having total mass greater than that of the original particle, which follows from energy conservation alone. Thus a proton

---

* The reactions $e^- + e^+ \to 2\gamma$ or 3γ are allowed by the conservation laws, and they happen.

can't decay into a neutron and something else, because protons are slightly lighter than neutrons. On the other hand, neutrons <u>can</u> (and <u>do</u>) decay into a proton, an electron, and a neutrino. A K-meson can decay into either two or three pi-mesons, but never into four, because the mass of four π's is greater than the mass of a K.

REFERENCES

1. Mass-energies and lifetimes are given for some particles in Appendix I.

2. Other decay and collision processes are described in many books and articles on elementary particles, such as

> <u>Elementary Particles</u> by Frisch and Thorndike, (D. Van Nostrand Co., Inc., 1964);

> <u>The World of Elementary Particles</u> by K. Ford (Blaisdell Publishing Co., 1963);

> "Elementary Particles" by Gell-Mann and Rosenbaum in <u>Scientific American</u> July, 1957;

> "Strongly Interacting Particles" by Chew, Gell-Mann and Rosenfeld in <u>Scientific American</u> February, 1964.

PROBLEMS XI

1. An Ω^- particle sometimes decays into a $\equiv^0$ hyperon and a pion, written $\Omega^- \rightarrow \equiv^0 + \pi^-$. The mass-energies are Ω^-: 1676 Mev; $\equiv^0$: 1311 Mev; $\pi-$: 140 Mev. Using energy units, find the pion's

   a. total energy
   b. kinetic energy
   c. momentum
   d. velocity

2. Calculate the frequency of the photons emitted in the π^0- decay:

   $$\pi^0 \rightarrow \gamma + \gamma.$$

3. A particular neutron decays in such a way that the final proton is at rest, while the electron and neutrino have equal and opposite momenta. Calculate this momentum.

4. A 10^6- kilogram spaceship fires a burst of laser light involving 10^{30} photons of wavelength λ = 4000 Angstroms. Find the recoil velocity of the ship.

5. A sodium D-line photon (λ = 5889 $\overset{o}{A}$) is scattered through an angle $\theta = 90^o$ by a free electron at rest. Find the change in wavelength of the scattered photon, and the kinetic energy of the recoil electron.

6. Explain why a photon which strikes a free electron cannot be absorbed: $\gamma + e \not\rightarrow e$. Such a reaction does take place if the electron is bound in an atom, and causes atomic excitation or even ejection of the electron from the atom. Why can absorption occur in this case?

7. It is possible to create antiprotons by the reaction $p + p \rightarrow p + p + p + \bar{p}$, where one of the initial protons comes from an accelerator, and the other is a nucleus in a liquid hydrogen bubble chamber. Find the "threshold energy" required; i.e., find the minimum energy of the incident proton needed to make the process go. It is helpful to see that for this energy the final particles will all move forward at the same velocity.

8. K^+- mesons can be photoproduced by the reaction

$$\gamma + p \rightarrow K^+ + \Lambda.$$

From the conservation laws, discover if it is possible for either the K^+ or Λ to be at rest in the laboratory (the rest-frame of the proton), and for what photon energy this could happen.

CHAPTER XII
MOMENTUM AND ENERGY TRANSFORMATION

THE MOMENTUM AND ENERGY of a particle depend, of course, on the frame of reference in which they are measured. For example, in the frame in which the particle is instantaneously at rest, it has no momentum, and its energy is entirely mass-energy mc^2. In any other frame, the particle has both momentum and kinetic energy. An important question therefore is this: if the momentum and energy of a particle are known in some one frame, how can they be found in some other frame? The answer to this question is particularly important in translating the analysis of collision processes between the laboratory and center-of-mass coordinate systems. With such a transformation, the collision and decay problems worked out in Chapter XI in the center-of-mass frame could be immediately applied to the laboratory reference frame as well. Also the momentum-energy transformation will allow us to derive the relativistic Doppler shift.

A. Derivation of the Transformation Law

One way to perform the transformation of momentum and energy is straightforward, but lengthy. Suppose, for example, we observe an object with momentum $\vec{p}$ and energy E. It follows that we also know the mass and velocity of the object through the equations

$$\vec{p} = \frac{m\vec{v}}{\sqrt{1 - v^2/c^2}} \quad \text{and } E = \frac{mc^2}{\sqrt{1 - v^2/c^2}} \, . \qquad \begin{matrix} (8-12) \\ (9-12) \end{matrix}$$

These equations can be solved for m and $\vec{v}$, most easily in practice by using

$$m^2 c^4 = E^2 - p^2 c^2 \text{ (to give the mass)} \qquad (9-13)$$

and

$$\vec{v} = \frac{\vec{p}c^2}{E} \qquad \text{(to give the three velocity components).} \qquad (9-22)$$

111

After finding the mass and velocity, the velocity $\vec{v'}$ of the object in a different (primed) frame can be calculated by the velocity transformation (7-11) of Chapter VII. Finally, the momentum and energy of the object in the primed frame can be found by substituting m and $\vec{v'}$ into

$$\vec{p'} = \frac{m\vec{v'}}{\sqrt{1 - v'^2/c^2}} \quad \text{and} \quad E' = \frac{mc^2}{\sqrt{1 - v'^2/c^2}} \ .$$

To take the simplest example, suppose the object is at rest in the unprimed frame, so that

$$\vec{v} = 0, \quad \vec{p} = 0, \quad E = mc^2. \tag{12-1}$$

Then by the velocity transformation,

$$v_x' = \frac{v_x - V}{1 - \dfrac{v_x V}{c^2}} = -V, \quad v_y' = v_z' = 0 \ , \tag{12-2}$$

which is what we would expect. So finally,

$$p_x = \frac{-mV}{\sqrt{1 - V^2/c^2}} \quad p_y' = p_z' = 0 \quad E' = \frac{mc^2}{\sqrt{1 - V^2/c^2}} \tag{12-3}$$

which are the momentum and energy of an object of mass $\underline{m}$ moving along the negative x' axis with velocity V. This transformation was easy, but any other case would have taken longer to work out.

Fortunately, it is possible to make these transformations once and for all, making it unnecessary to do the algebra over and over. That is, if the momentum and energy of a particle in any one frame are known, they can be immediately found in any other frame without going through the process of calculating the velocities, transforming them, etc. As the first step in doing all the algebra in general, we will show that

$$\frac{1}{\sqrt{1 - v'^2/c^2}} = \frac{1 - v_x V/c^2}{\sqrt{1 - v^2/c^2}\sqrt{1 - V^2/c^2}} \ . \tag{12-4}$$

112

That is, we know that $1 - v'^2/c^2 = 1 - (v_x'^2 + v_y'^2 + v_z'^2)/c^2$

$$= 1 - \frac{1}{c^2(1-v_x V/c^2)^2} \left[(v_x-V)^2 + (v_y^2 + v_z^2)(1-V^2/c^2) \right],$$

found by using the velocity transformation equations for v_x', v_y', and v_z'. Putting everything over a common denominator and expanding, this is

$$\frac{(c^2-2v_x V + v_x^2 V^2/c^2) - \left\{ v_x^2 + v_y^2 + v_z^2 - 2v_x V + V^2 - \frac{V^2}{c^2}(v_y^2 + v_z^2) \right\}}{c^2 (1-v_x V/c^2)^2}$$

$$= \frac{c^2 - V^2 - v^2(1-V^2/c^2)}{c^2 (1-v_x V/c^2)^2} = \frac{(1-v^2/c^2)(1-V^2/c^2)}{(1-v_x V/c^2)^2}$$

which is the relation we wanted to prove.

It then follows immediately that

$$E' \equiv \frac{mc^2}{\sqrt{1 - v'^2/c^2}} = \frac{mc^2 - mv_x V}{\sqrt{1 - v^2/c^2}\,\sqrt{1 - V^2/c^2}} = \frac{E - Vp_x}{\sqrt{1 - V^2/c^2}}$$

which is the first of the sought-after transformation rules. Also

$$p_x' \equiv \frac{mv_x'}{\sqrt{1 - v'^2/c^2}} = \frac{m(v_x-V)}{1 - v_x V/c^2} \cdot \frac{1 - v_x V/c^2}{\sqrt{1 - v^2/c^2}\,\sqrt{1 - V^2/c^2}}$$

$$= \frac{p_x - (V/c^2)\,E}{\sqrt{1 - V^2/c^2}}$$

$$p_y' \equiv \frac{mv_y'}{\sqrt{1 - v'^2/c^2}} = \frac{mv_y \sqrt{1 - V^2/c^2}}{\sqrt{1 - v^2/c^2}\,\sqrt{1 - V^2/c^2}} = p_y$$

$$p_z' \equiv \frac{mv_z'}{\sqrt{1 - v'^2/c^2}} = \frac{mv_z \sqrt{1 - V^2/c^2}}{\sqrt{1 - v^2/c^2}\,\sqrt{1 - V^2/c^2}} = p_z$$

or altogether

113

$$p_x' = \gamma \left(p_x - \frac{V}{c^2} E\right)$$

$$p_y' = p_y$$

$$p_z' = p_z \tag{12-5}$$

$$E' = \gamma (E - Vp_x)$$

where $\gamma = 1/\sqrt{1 - V^2/c^2}$

which are collectively called the energy-momentum transformation. If $\vec{p}$ and E are known, $\vec{p}'$ and E' follow right away.

The transformation is easy to remember, because it is very similar to the Lorentz transformation for x, y, z, and t. The only difference is the number of c's in the first and last equations, which can always be fixed by checking dimensions. To do our trivial example over again, $\vec{v} = 0$, so $\vec{p} = 0$ and $E = mc^2$. Then

$$p_x' = -\gamma \frac{V}{c^2} mc^2 = \frac{-mV}{\sqrt{1 - V^2/c^2}}$$

$$p_y' = p_z' = 0 \tag{12-6}$$

$$E' = \gamma E = \frac{mc^2}{\sqrt{1 - V^2/c^2}}.$$

We can write down the inverse transformation just as we did for the Lorentz transformation, by interchanging the primed and unprimed variables and changing the sign of V. This gives

$$p_x = \gamma \left(p_x' + \frac{V}{c^2} E'\right)$$

$$p_y = p_y' \qquad p_z = p_z'$$

$$E = \gamma (E' + Vp_x') \tag{12-7}$$

where $\gamma = 1/\sqrt{1 - V^2/c^2}$.

As an example of actually using the transformation in practice, consider again the decay of the K^0 meson into two π^0's, which we employed

114

originally to find the expression for relativistic energy. Now suppose that the K^O meson is moving, which is usually true in the laboratory. As a particular case, let the K^O be moving at velocity $v = \frac{3}{5}$ c, and let it decay into one π^O moving forward (in the direction the K^O was moving) and another π^O moving backward. We would like to know the momentum and energy of each pion. One way to solve this problem would be to conserve momentum and energy, using the same procedure as in Chapter XI. But since we have already solved it in the center-of-mass frame, it is much easier to employ the momentum-energy transformation.

To set up the problem in a systematic way, suppose the K^O moves to the right in the laboratory, that pion number <u>one</u> is emitted <u>forward</u>, and pion number <u>two</u> is emitted <u>backward</u>, as shown in Figure 12.1. By convention the primed frame moves to the right, so the center-of-mass frame will be the primed frame. For this frame we found in Chapter IX the momentum and energy of each particle. The results were:

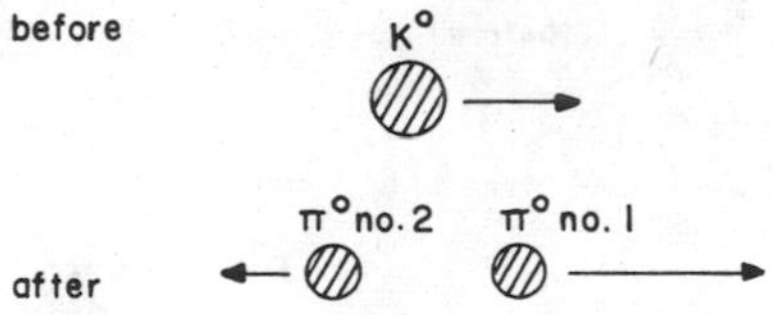

Figure 12.1

	momentum $\vec{p'}$	energy E'
K^O meson	0	498 Mev
π^O no. 1	210 Mev/c	249 Mev
π^O no. 2	-210 Mev/c	249 Mev

Now the energies and momenta in the laboratory (unprimed) frame can be found by applying the inverse momentum-energy transformation. The relative velocity of the two frames is $V = \frac{3}{5}$ c, so

$$\gamma = \frac{1}{\sqrt{1 - (3/5)^2}} = 5/4,$$

giving $p_x = \frac{5}{4} (p_x' + \frac{3}{5} E'/c)$ and $E = \frac{5}{4} (E' + \frac{3}{5} c\, p_x').$

Solving for p_x and E for each particle, the laboratory values are found
to be

	momentum $\vec{p}$	Energy E
K^0 meson	373 Mev/c	623 Mev
π^0 no. 1	449 Mev/c	469 Mev
π^0 no. 2	-76 Mev/c	154 Mev

As a good check on the results, notice that energy and momentum are
conserved in this frame as well.

The results are summarized in Figure 12.2.

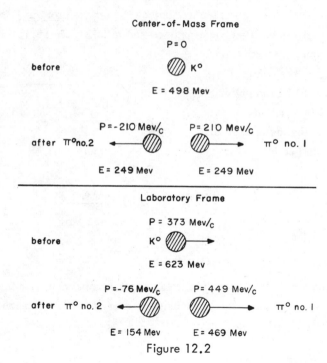

Figure 12.2

B. The Relativistic Doppler Effect

The momentum-energy transformation can also be used to find the relativistic Doppler shift for light. Everyone is familiar with the Doppler
shift of sound-waves — the apparent frequency of a source depends upon

its velocity with respect to the observer. The Doppler effect has long been known to hold for light-waves also. A radiating source emits light which appears to an observer to be shifted to <u>higher</u> frequencies if the source is moving <u>toward</u> him, and to <u>lower</u> frequencies if the source is moving <u>away</u> from him. The shift is very small in most situations, so it can only be detected by making careful spectroscopic measurements.

The best-known situation in which the Doppler effect for light is observed is in the shift in the line-spectra of stars. Most stars or galaxies are moving with respect to us, so that the wavelengths in their spectra are somewhat shifted toward the blue or red. In fact, very distant galaxies are always found to be red-shifted, which is the principal evidence for the idea that the universe is expanding. Within experimental errors, the amount of red-shift increases linearly with the distance of the galaxy, so that more distant galaxies are moving away faster. This is what we would expect if the universe as we know it resulted from a "big bang" explosion at some time in the past — faster-moving objects would be further away. The largest measured red-shifts come from sources which are apparently moving away from us at as much as about 8/10 the speed of light. An example of a red-shifted spectra is shown in the photograph of Figure 12.3. It is from a "quasar" (quasi-stellar radio source 3C273), one of a number of recently discovered objects which are not well understood.[*]

The Doppler effect is also one cause of line-broadening in the spectra of hot gases, and has been observed in the laboratory as well as in the spectra of the sun and stars. The average energy of the molecules in a hot diffuse gas is proportional to the temperature. So, the hotter the gas, the more Doppler shift we would expect in the radiation emitted from the molecules. At any given time some molecules will be approaching and some receding from an observer, so that the net effect is to broaden each spectral line to include a larger range of wavelengths.

---

[*] Most astrophysicists believe that quasar red-shifts are caused by the Doppler effect, although some believe they may be gravitational red-shifts of the type discussed in Appendix D.

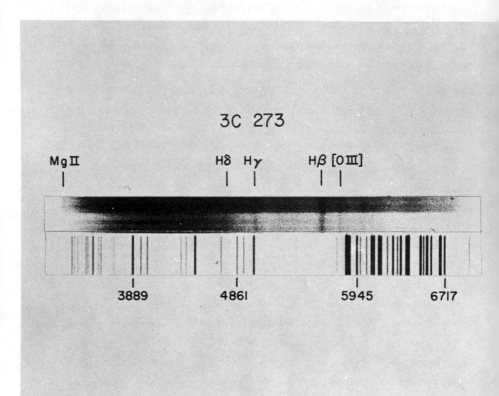

Figure 12.3

Spectrum of 3C 273, courtesy of Dr. Maarten Schmidt, Mt. Wilson and Palomar Observatories.

The quasar spectrum is at the top, and a comparison spectrum is underneath it. Note that the H_γ line of hydrogen, which has a normal wavelength of 4340 Angstroms, has been red-shifted to more than 5000 Angstroms.

118

A relativistically correct formula for the Doppler shift, in terms of the relative velocity of the source and observer, can be easily found from the transformation laws of energy and momentum. Consider a source which is at rest in the unprimed coordinate system, and which emits a photon at some angle θ with respect to the x-axis. We can assume that this photon is in the x-y plane, as shown in Figure 12.4. If the photon frequency is ν, its energy is $E = h\nu$ and its momentum is $p = E/c = h\nu/c$. In terms of components,

$$p_x = \frac{h\nu}{c} \cos \theta$$

$$p_y = \frac{h\nu}{c} \sin \theta$$

$$p_z = 0$$

$$E = h\nu.$$

(12-8)

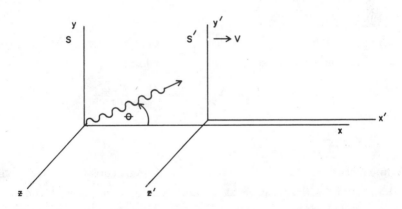

Figure 12.4

Now suppose the observer is at rest in the primed frame, which by the usual convention is moving to the right at speed V. He will find that the photon has energy E', momentum $\vec{p}'$, and angle θ' with respect to the x'-axis. Each of these parameters can be calculated from the transformation laws. That is,

$$p_x' = \frac{h\nu'}{c} \cos \theta' = \gamma (p_x - VE/c^2) = \gamma (h\nu/c \cos \theta - V/c^2\ h\nu)$$

$$\text{or } \nu' \cos \theta' = \gamma\nu (\cos \theta - V/c)$$

(12-9)

119

$$p_y' = \frac{h\nu'}{c} \sin \theta' = p_y = \frac{h\nu}{c} \sin \theta$$

$$p_z' = p_z = 0$$

(12-9 continued)

$$E' = h\nu' = \gamma (E - Vp_x) = \gamma (h\nu - V/c\, h\nu \cos \theta)$$

or $\nu' = \gamma\nu\, (1 - V/c \cos \theta)$.

The frequencies can be eliminated by dividing the fourth equation into the first, to give

$$\cos \theta' = \frac{\cos \theta - V/c}{1 - V/c \cos \theta}, \tag{12-10}$$

which expresses the photon angle in the primed frame in terms of its angle in the unprimed frame. These angles are clearly different (except when $\theta = 0$ or π), which is just the aberration of light effect discussed in Chapter II. The result can be turned around to give θ in terms of θ':

$$\cos \theta = \frac{\cos \theta' + V/c}{1 + V/c \cos \theta'} . \tag{12-11}$$

Using this relation, the unprimed angle in the fourth of equations (12-9) can be eliminated to obtain the Doppler formula:[*]

$$\nu' = \gamma\nu \left\{ 1 - \frac{V}{c} \left(\frac{\cos \theta' + V/c}{1 + V/c \cos \theta'} \right) \right\} = \frac{\gamma\,\nu\,(1 - V^2/c^2)}{1 + V/c \cos \theta'}$$

$$\text{or } \nu' = \frac{\nu\sqrt{1 - V^2/c^2}}{1 + V/c \cos \theta'} . \tag{12-12}$$

This equation says that if a source moves at total velocity V from our point of view, with a component of velocity away from us of $V \cos \theta'$, we will see frequency ν' if the source emits frequency ν in its own frame. For velocities much lower than c, the second-order term in V/c can be dropped to give

---

[*] In deriving the result, we have assumed that the momentum-energy transformation is correct for massless photons, even though it was derived for massive particles in part A. Our assumption is shown to be correct in the more advanced books listed in the general bibliography, using relativistic electromagnetism. It is certainly a very plausible assumption in the context of Chapter XIII.

$$\nu' = \frac{\nu}{1 + \dfrac{V}{c} \cos \theta'} \; . \qquad\qquad (12\text{-}13)$$

This is the non-relativistic Doppler formula for a moving source, which can be easily derived without relativity theory.[*]

An interesting special case of the relativistic Doppler formula occurs when the source moves at right angles to our line of sight, neither approaching nor receding. Setting $\theta = \pi/2$, the observed frequency is $\nu' = \nu\sqrt{1 - V^2/c^2}$. The fact that there is a frequency shift from sources moving sideways is a relativistic result which is not present in the non-relativistic formula. This "transverse Doppler effect" is easily understood from time-dilation. Everything on a moving source will seem to us to be running slow in time, including the atoms responsible for the radiation. Therefore the frequency of the emitted light, which serves as a kind of clock demonstrating the time-rate on the source, will be decreased by the time-dilation factor $\sqrt{1 - V^2/c^2}$.

Other important special cases are when the source moves directly toward us or away from us. If it is moving away, $\theta' = 0$, so $\nu' = \nu\sqrt{\dfrac{1 - V/c}{1 + V/c}} < \nu$, corresponding to a red-shift. If it is coming toward us, $\theta = \pi$, so $\nu' = \sqrt{\dfrac{1 + V/c}{1 - V/c}} > \nu$, corresponding to a blue-shift. If for example a distant galaxy is moving away from us at half the speed of light, we will observe a lower frequency for each spectral line: $\nu' = \nu\sqrt{\dfrac{1 - 1/2}{1 + 1/2}} = \nu/\sqrt{3}$.

The relativistic Doppler formula was checked experimentally by Ives and Stilwell in 1938.[†] The most obvious way to differentiate the relativistic from the non-relativistic effect would be to look for the transverse Doppler shift, which would be zero if the classical formula were correct. Unfortunately, this is an effect of second order in V/c:

$$\nu' = \nu \sqrt{1 - V^2/c^2} \cong \nu (1 - V^2/2c^2) \; . \qquad\qquad (12\text{-}14)$$

---

* cf. Fundamentals of Optics, Jenkins and White (McGraw-Hill), 1957).

† H. E. Ives and G. R. Stilwell, J. Opt. Soc. Am. 28, 215, 1938.

121

Therefore, unless the angle θ in the general formula is precisely 90°, the first-order term $V/c \cos \theta$ in the denominator will swamp the second-order term. For this reason, Ives and Stilwell measured the longitudinal Doppler effect instead. They looked at the light emitted forward and backward ($\theta = 0$ or π) by a beam of moving hydrogen atoms. Classical theory would predict (since $\lambda = c/\nu$):

$$\lambda' = \lambda (1 \pm V/c) \text{ for } \theta = 0 \text{ or } \pi , \tag{12-15}$$

and relativity predicts:

$$\lambda' = \lambda \frac{(1 \pm V/c)}{\sqrt{1 - V^2/c^2}} \cong \lambda (1 \pm V/c + \frac{V^2}{2c^2}) \text{ for } \theta = 0 \text{ or } \pi \tag{12-16}$$

(for small V/c, using the binomial expansion).

Therefore, the difference in each case between the relativistic and classical result is $\delta\lambda' = \frac{1}{2} \lambda V^2/c^2$. A recent repetition of the experiment with greater accuracy was done by Mandelberg and Witten in 1961.[*] They found experimentally that $\delta\lambda' = (0.498 \pm 0.025) \lambda V^2/c^2$, implying an experimental precision of 5%. Therefore this experiment provides a very good confirmation of the relativistic Doppler formula.

REFERENCES

1. It is interesting that there are two classical Doppler-shift formulas in classical physics, one for a moving source and one for a moving observer. These two situations are indistinguishable according to relativity, and the single relativistic formula is halfway between the two classical formulas. This is discussed in Jenkins and White Fundamentals of Optics (McGraw Hill, 1957).

2. Checking Einstein's prediction for the Doppler shift is reported in articles by Ives and Stilwell, J. Opt. Soc. Am. 28, 215 (1938) and by Mandelberg and Witten, J. Opt. Soc. Am. 52, 529 (1962).

---

[*] H. I. Mandelberg and L. Witten, J. Opt. Soc. Am. 52, 529, 1962.

PROBLEMS XII

1. An electron of mass $.511$ Mev/c^2 moves along our $+x$-axis at speed $v = \frac{3}{5} c$. Find its momentum and energy in our frame, and also in a frame moving to the right at speed $V = \frac{4}{5} c$.

2. The decay of the Λ-hyperon was discussed in Chapter XI, and the momentum and energy of the emitted proton and pion were calculated in the center of mass frame, in terms of the particle masses. Now suppose the initial Λ moves to the right in the laboratory with speed $V = \frac{4}{5} c$, and also suppose the decay pion moves to the right in the center of mass frame. Find the energy and momentum of the pion in both the center of mass and laboratory frames of reference, in Mev units.

3. A comet approaches the earth at speed $v = 3 \times 10^5$ meters/sec. Calculate the fractional Doppler shift $\Delta\nu/\nu$ due to this velocity.

4. The radius of the sun is 7×10^8 meters, and its equatorial rotation period is 24.6 days. Find the shift in wavelength of 5000 Å light, due to the Doppler shift, between parts of the sun moving toward us and away from us, due to its rotation. Is the relativistic correction $\sqrt{1 - v^2/c^2}$ important in this case, if we want 1% accuracy?

CHAPTER XIII

SPACETIME

IN CLASSICAL PHYSICS, space and time never get mixed up. The two concepts are separate and distinct; there isn't even any particular reason to mention them both in the same sentence. The Galilean transformation of classical mechanics can be written with the time equation off to one side, or even left out entirely because it is so trivial:

$$x' = x - Vt \qquad\qquad t' = t$$
$$y' = y \qquad\qquad\qquad\qquad\qquad\qquad (1\text{-}1)$$
$$z' = z$$

The transformation guarantees that the time any event happens is the same in all inertial frames, and that the length of an object is likewise an absolute quantity.

In relativistic physics, however, space and time become thoroughly intertwined through the Lorentz transformation:

$$x' = \gamma\,(x - Vt)$$
$$y' = y$$
$$z' = z \qquad\qquad\qquad\qquad\qquad\qquad (7\text{-}6)$$
$$t' = \gamma\,\left(t - \frac{Vx}{c^2}\right)\,.$$

Here the time equation is as important as the others, and cannot be retired to the side to be considered separately. Time intervals and space intervals aren't the same to all observers, but instead become mixed with each other. What is purely a distance to one observer may correspond to both a distance and a time interval to an observer in a different frame of reference. This situation sounds much like viewing an object in ordinary space from two different angles — how much of an object is in its "height," "breadth," or "depth" depends on the point of view. A meter-stick which is in the x-direction to one observer may be partly in the y-direction to an observer using a rotated coordinate system. If the two sets of coordinates have the same origin, but are relatively rotated by an angle θ, the coordinates of a point in the

primed system are given in terms of the coordinates of the same point
in the unprimed system by the equations

$$x' = \cos \theta \; x + \sin \theta \; y$$
$$y' = -\sin \theta \; x + \cos \theta \; y \qquad\qquad (13\text{-}1)$$

as shown in Figure 13-1.

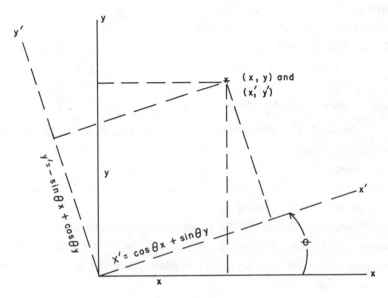

Figure 13-1

The primed coordinates are linear combinations of the unprimed coordinates. The coordinates in one system get "mixed up" in another
system.

Neglecting for a moment the y and z directions, the Lorentz transformation (7-6) assumes a very similar form:

$$x' = \gamma \; x - \gamma \; V \; t$$
$$t' = \frac{-\gamma V}{c^2} x + \gamma \; t \qquad\qquad (13\text{-}2)$$

which looks like a kind of rotation in an "x-t plane." This analogy between the x-t Lorentz transformation and a rotation is certainly not
perfect, for two reasons. First of all, any of the coefficients, γ, γV,

125

or $\gamma V/c^2$ can exceed unity, so cannot be identified as sines or cosines. (The latter two coefficients are not even dimensionless, which can be traced to the fact that x and t have different dimensions.) Also, the sign of the second term on the right-hand side of the x'-equation is different from the sign in the rotation equations. In spite of these difficulties, since x and t are so closely coupled it might be useful to think of them as coordinates in some kind of space having unusual rules for rotation. If y and z are thrown in as well, we would have a four-dimensional "spacetime," in which the Lorentz transformation plays the role of a rotation between coordinate systems. Time and space are a matter of perspective in this space, the amount of each depending on the "angle" from which it is viewed.

It was Hermann Minkowski who invented this kind of space in 1908, and thereby made one of the biggest contributions to relativity theory after Einstein's original work. He showed that four-dimensional spacetime is very useful, and that the whole theory of Einstein becomes simpler and much more elegant when looked at in this way. The classical separation of space and time is unnatural and somewhat artificial in relativity. To quote Minkowski, "space by itself, and time by itself, are doomed to fade away into mere shadows, and only a kind of union of the two will survive."[*]

The idea of spacetime, or "Minkowski space" has not only been important as a useful and elegant format for special relativity, but it was essential in Einstein's later construction of his general theory. There he carried it beyond the "flat" or "Euclidean-like" spacetime we are discussing here, and investigated the consequence of allowing this space to be curved. The results showed that the phenomenon of gravitation can be ascribed to such a space curvature.

Ordinary three-dimensional space is populated with all kinds of "real" and more-or-less abstract physical quantities, which can be classified according to how they change when the coordinates are rotated. Thus a

---

[*] See reference 1.

126

scalar (like the temperature at some point, or the mass of a particle) can be represented by a single number which is not changed upon going to another system of coordinates. A vector (like a particle's position vector $\vec{r}$ or momentum $\vec{p}$) is represented by three numbers, corresponding to the x, y, and z components of the vector. Upon rotation of the coordinates, the components will change as a function of the rotation angle. If, for example, we want to know the components of an arbitrary vector $\vec{p}$ in a primed frame obtained by rotating the coordinate system through an angle θ about the z-axis, then

$$p_x' = \cos \theta \, p_x + \sin \theta \, p_y$$

$$p_y' = -\sin \theta \, p_x + \cos \theta \, p_y \qquad (13\text{-}3)$$

$$p_z' = p_z.$$

Although the components change, it is nevertheless true that the length of the vector itself doesn't depend on the coordinate system from which it is viewed: i.e. $|\vec{p'}| = |\vec{p}|$, or alternatively the sum of the squares of the components is invariant: $p_x'^2 + p_y'^2 + p_z'^2 = p_x^2 + p_y^2 + p_z^2$. This invariance is easily verified in the special case of the rotation about the z-axis just mentioned.

In going to four-dimensional spacetime, physical quantities have to be re-examined to find out how they transform. We want to identify those which do not change under a Lorentz transformation (called "four-scalars") and those which change like the coordinates themselves (called "four-vectors"). The mass m and electric charge q of a particle are examples of four-scalars. The simplest four-vector is the coordinate vector itself, with components x, y, z, and t. Actually we would certainly like to require that all four components of a vector have the same dimensions, which can be satisfied in this case by multiplying the time t by the speed of light c, so as to give the fourth component the dimensions of distance.[*] Having done this, we would hope that this four-vector has the same kind of properties as ordinary

---

[*] Alternatively, we would measure time in "light-seconds," the distance light travels in one second, and forget the factor c.

vectors in three-dimensional space. For example, the absolute length of the vector (or alternatively, the sum of squares of the components) should be the same in all frames. But unfortunately, it is simple to show directly from the Lorentz transformation that

$$x'^2 + y'^2 + z'^2 + (ct')^2 \neq x^2 + y^2 + z^2 + (ct)^2 \qquad (13\text{-}4)$$

which <u>might</u> make a lesser mathematician than Minkowski give up at once.

It appears that the word "vector" is not appropriate for the components x, y, z, ct. However, recall from Chapter VIII that another combination, $x^2 + y^2 + z^2 - c^2 t^2$ <u>is</u> invariant! Namely, just by using the Lorentz transformation, the equation

$$x'^2 + y'^2 + z'^2 - c^2 t'^2 = x^2 + y^2 + z^2 - c^2 t^2 \qquad (13\text{-}5)$$

is seen to be an identity. In the particular case of a spherical wave-front that starts from the origin of both frames, each side of the equation is zero. In other cases, where the coordinated specify the position of an arbitrary object, this sum of squares (with a minus sign for the time component) will not be zero, but <u>will</u> be the <u>same</u> in all inertial frames.

So in order to hold on to the nice properties of vectors, we can patch up our theory a little by claiming that the four components of the co-ordinate four-vector should be (x, y, z, ict), with the imaginary number "i" inserted in order to get a minus sign when the fourth component is squared. The presence of an imaginary time component should not be taken as a matter of deep philosophical significance, since it was only put in so as to make four-vectors in Minkowski space behave like vectors we are used to. It does show, however, that even though we are trying to say that space and time are in some respects similar, they are nevertheless not completely equivalent, but maintain a certain degree of individuality. No one should have been surprised that four-vectors differ somewhat from ordinary vectors, because it has already been pointed out that the Lorentz transformation is not an ordinary rotation, since the coefficients exceed unity and there is a sign difference as well. For convenience, we can label the coordinates (x_1, x_2, x_3, x_4), where $x_1 = x$, $x_2 = y$, $x_3 = z$, and $x_4 = ict$. Then a "rotation" in the "x-t plane," corresponding to a Lorentz transformation between our usual primed and unprimed frames, can be written

$$x_1' = \gamma x_1 + i \gamma \frac{V}{c} x_4$$

$$x_2' = x_2$$

$$x_3' = x_3 \qquad\qquad (13\text{-}6)$$

$$x_4' = -i \gamma \frac{V}{c} x_1 + \gamma x_4$$

which is just the usual transformation in a somewhat disguised form. The coefficients in these equations indicate how a four-vector transforms under a rotation in the x-t plane. If we can identify four quantities which transform with the same coefficients, then those four quantities are the components of a four-vector.

An obvious candidate for another four-vector is one consisting of the components of the momentum $\vec{p}$ and the energy E. In Chapter XII it was shown that the momentum-energy transformation is very similar to the Lorentz transformation. Now we know that this was no accident, but that momentum and energy were ripe for combining into a single four-vector. In order to use the transformation coefficients just derived, we again have to make the fourth component imaginary, and also divide E by c to give it dimensions of momentum. The "momentum-energy four-vector" is therefore

$$p_\mu \text{ (where } \mu = 1, 2, 3, 4) = (p_1, p_2, p_3, p_4) = (p_x, p_y, p_z, iE/c)$$

which must transform as

$$p_1' = \gamma p_1 + i \gamma \frac{V}{c} p_4$$

$$p_2' = p_2$$

$$p_3' = p_3 \qquad\qquad (13\text{-}7)$$

$$p_4' = -i \gamma \frac{V}{c} p_1 + \gamma p_4.$$

Substituting in the values of the four components, these equations are identical with the momentum-energy transformation of Chapter XII.

If p_μ is really a four-vector, it must also be true that its square is an invariant. The sum of squares of the four components is

$$\Sigma p_\mu^{\ 2} = p_x^{\ 2} + p_y^{\ 2} + p_x^{\ 2} - E^2/c^2 \qquad (13\text{-}8)$$

which will be recognized as part of the relation

$$E^2 = \vec{p}^2 c^2 + m^2 c^4 = (p_x^{\ 2} + p_y^{\ 2} + p_z^{\ 2})\, c^2 + m^2 c^4 \qquad (9\text{-}13)$$

between the energy and momentum of a particle of mass m. So $\Sigma p_\mu^{\ 2} = -m^2 c^2$, which is indeed an invariant, since m is a scalar. That is, for arbitrary primed and unprimed frames

$$p_x^{\ 2} + p_y^{\ 2} + p_z^{\ 2} - E^2/c^2 = p_x'^{\ 2} + p_y'^{\ 2} + p_z'^{\ 2} - E'^2/c^2 = -m^2 c^2. \quad (13\text{-}9)$$

That the square of a four-vector can be negative is a result of having an imaginary fourth component.

The close bonding of momentum and energy has the bonus feature of unifying the two conservation laws. For if, say, momentum but not energy were conserved in one particular reference frame, then not even momentum could be conserved in another frame, since it is a linear combination of energy and momentum from the original frame.

Although we won't go further here, many other quantities can be written as four-vectors, and the fundamental laws of relativistic mechanics and electromagnetism are particularly simple and compact when written in four-dimensional form. Some extension of this program is carried out in Chapter XIV.

The introduction of four-dimensional spacetime is clearly not a terribly mystical step. It provides a point of view which makes a lot of sense, because relativistic physics becomes simpler and more elegant, and also because it unifies concepts which were previously thought to be independent. Nobody can imagine four-dimensional spacetime in the same way that everybody grasps three-dimensional space. The chief method one uses to understand it is by mathematics and by drawing pictures and becoming well acquainted with situations described by the mathematics.

For example, since we can't draw a picture of four-dimensional space-time, we can at least draw pictures with one space and one time dimension. Let the time axis be vertical and the space axis be horizontal. Then in this space, a light ray would look as shown in Figure 13.2. If in particular the space axis corresponds to the x-axis in three-space, the line would represent a light ray moving in the + x-direction. A line with the opposite slope would represent a ray moving in the - x-direction. If we add one more space-axis (say the y-axis) projecting out of the page,

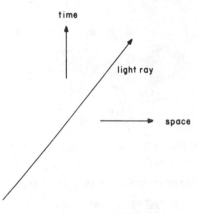

Figure 13.2

and take the locus of all light rays passing through some given point, they would form a cone, as shown in Figure 13.3.

We can't imagine adding the z-axis as well, but we can still call the locus of all rays through a particular spacetime point the "light-cone."

What about particles other than photons? Any massive particle moves with velocity v<c, so the line for any particle which passes through the vertex of the cone (which we'll call the origin) must be "trapped" inside the light-cone. That is, $\frac{x}{t}$ must be larger for light than for any massive particle, so the line for a particle (called its "world-line") might look as shown in Figure 13.4, where at no time is its vertical slope less than that of a light ray.

Suppose we consider the particle when it is at the origin in the space-time diagram. The absolute past of the particle consists of all events

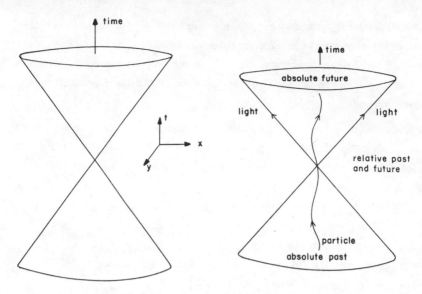

Figure 13.3   Figure 13.4

within or on the <u>lower</u> light-cone. No event <u>outside</u> the cone could have influenced the particle in any way, since the influence would have had to propagate faster than light in order to reach the particle. Similarly, the <u>absolute future</u> for the particle consists of all events within or on the <u>upper</u> light-cone. For the particle cannot escape from this cone, nor can it influence any event outside the cone. So the region outside either cone is actually some kind of limbo which we'll call the <u>relative</u> past and future. For any event in this region is at time t > 0 in some frames, and at t < 0 in other frames. The relativity of simultaneity cannot allow us to say that any particular event outside the light-cone is definitely in the past or definitely in the future.

As a particular example, suppose the sun blew up nine minutes ago in our frame of reference. That event is definitely in our absolute past, since the sun is only about eight light-minutes away. <u>Any</u> observer, no matter <u>how</u> fast he is moving, will agree that the explosion was in our past, either by checking his clocks or just by looking at its effect upon us. But suppose the sun blew up only <u>two</u> minutes ago. That event is <u>not</u> in our absolute past, since it has not been able to influence us. Although it is in the past in <u>our</u> frame of reference, there are

132

inertial frames in which the explosion occurs <u>after</u> what is "right now" to us on the earth. (Needless to say, in about six minutes the explosion <u>will</u> be in our absolute past.) In our frame of reference, the sequence of events is shown in Figure 13.5. Let the sun be at the origin x = 0,

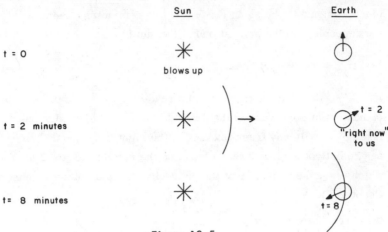

Figure 13.5

and the earth be at x = D = 8 light-minutes. In our frame the sun explodes at t = 0, "right now" is at t = 2 minutes, and light reaches the earth at t = 8 minutes.

In a primed frame moving to the right at speed V, the Lorentz time transformation gives

$$t' = \gamma (t - Vx/c^2)$$

so in the primed frame the sun-time is

$$t'_{sun} = \gamma \, t_{sun}$$

and earth-time is

$$t'_{earth} = \gamma (t_{earth} - VD/c^2).$$

To <u>primed</u> observers, at any instant $t'_{sun} = t'_{earth}$, so canceling the γ-factors,

$$t_{sun} = t_{earth} - V \, D/c^2$$

133

or

$$t_{sun} = t_{earth} - 8\frac{V}{c} \text{ (in minutes)},$$

which is a relation between the readings of clocks fixed to the sun and earth as read at any particular instant in the primed frame. When the clock attached to the earth reads t_{earth} = 2 minutes ("right now" to earth people), in the primed frame the sun clock is seen to read only

$$t_{sun} = 2 - 8\frac{V}{c} \text{ minutes}.$$

If $\frac{V}{c} > \frac{1}{4}$, the clock fixed on the sun reads less than t = 0, so from the standpoint of observers in the primed frame, the explosion hasn't yet taken place! In any frame moving to the right with speed V > c/4, the sun hasn't yet exploded when clocks on the earth read t = 2 minutes, which is another example of the relativity of simultaneity discussed in Chapter VI.

It is straightforward to prove that there is no frame in which the sun has failed to explode when earth-clocks read t_{earth} = 8 minutes. For

$$t_{sun} = t_{earth} - 8\frac{V}{c}$$

relates the readings of clocks fixed to the sun and earth as viewed by primed observers. If t_{earth} = 8 minutes, $t_{sun} \geq 0$ even as V → c. Thus for $t_{earth} \geq 8$ minutes, the explosion is in the absolute past.

The converse way of thinking about this result is also enlightening. If we demand that the effect on an object be preceded by its cause in all frames of reference, then no frame can move with speed V ≥ c with respect to any other frame. The effects of the sun exploding reach the earth at t = 8 minutes. So if we demand that the explosion must have happened (i.e. $t_{sun} > 0$) when t_{earth} = 8 minutes, then $8 - \frac{8V}{c} > 0$, implying V < c. Relativity is therefore consistent with a universal cause-effect time ordering. Even though simultaneity is relative, causes precede effects in all frames of reference.

134

REFERENCES

1. Spacetime is introduced by Minkowski in "Space and Time" translated in The Principle of Relativity by Einstein and others (Dover Publications, 1923).

2. Several of the books listed in the General Bibliography discuss four-vectors in great detail. These include references 2, 4, 5, and 6.

PROBLEMS XIII

1. Show explicitly that the time derivative $\dfrac{dp_\mu}{dt}$ of the four-vector p_μ is not itself a four-vector.

2. Show by constructing an example that if a signal were to propagate from a to b faster than the speed of light in our frame of reference, there would exist frames in which the signal reaches b before it left a.

3. The squared "interval" between two events in spacetime is given by $\Delta s^2 = \Delta x^2 + \Delta y^2 + \Delta z^2 - c^2 \Delta t^2$, where Δx is the difference in the x-coordinate of the two events, etc. If $\Delta s^2 > 0$, the interval is said to be spacelike, and if $\Delta s^2 < 0$, the interval is said to be timelike. Show that if an interval is spacelike (timelike) in one frame of reference, it is spacelike (timelike) in all frames of reference.

CHAPTER XIV
RELATIVISTIC FORCES

IT WAS MENTIONED in Chapter VIII that Newton's equation of motion $\vec{F} = m\,\vec{a}$ may not be true in relativistic mechanics. Our first goal in this chapter is to find the correct equation relating relativistic force and motion. In order to do so, we have to know at least one force which acts in a known way on relativistic particles. We can't assume that familiar forces will fill the bill. For example, a carefully constructed spring may exert a force $F = -kx$ on a slowly moving object, but it may not exert the same force on an object moving at relativistic speeds. Likewise, the force $F = mg$ of a uniform gravitational field may not apply when relativistic particles are being considered. That is why the subject of electromagnetism is taken up here along with force and the relativistic equation of motion. The effect of electric and magnetic fields on fast particles is well known in the laboratory, and the forces of external fields on charged particles are well understood. So electric and magnetic forces will be used as an example of relativistic forces.

Aside from this convenience of introducing electromagnetic forces, the connection between relativity and electromagnetism is important in itself. Actually it was largely through his study of electromagnetism that Einstein uncovered special relativity — for relativity in a sense is implicitly contained in electromagnetic theory as developed by Maxwell and others in the nineteenth century. A good treatment of this subject requires more background in electricity and magnetism than is assumed here, but we will take up the subject to some extent in Appendix G.

The non-relativistic equation of motion of a particle of mass m is given by Newton as

$$\vec{F} = \frac{d\vec{p}}{dt} \tag{14-1}$$

or $\vec{F} = m\,\vec{a}$, since classically $\vec{p} = m\vec{v}$, and $\frac{d\vec{v}}{dt} = \vec{a}$. To find out how the particle moves, in principle it is only necessary to know the forces exerted on it. In particular, an electrically charged particle in an

136

electromagnetic field is found experimentally to obey the equation of motion

$$\frac{d\vec{p}}{dt} = q \, (\vec{E} + \vec{v} \times \vec{B}) \tag{14-2}$$

where q is the charge, $\vec{E}$ and $\vec{B}$ are the electric and magnetic fields at the point of space-time where the particle is located, $\vec{v}$ is the particle's velocity, and everything is written in MKS units. $\vec{E}$ and $\vec{B}$ are vector fields, represented by arrows at each point in space, and may change with time. The electromagnetic force is therefore

$$\vec{F} = q \, (\vec{E} + \vec{v} \times \vec{B}), \tag{14-3}$$

which is often called the "Lorentz force." The electric force is independent of the particle's motion, while the magnetic force only acts if the particle is moving. Because of this property, and because the velocity of a particle depends upon the frame of reference, it is reasonable that electric and magnetic fields may change from one frame to another. In Appendix G, we'll be able to write down the transformation laws for $\vec{E}$ and $\vec{B}$.

A non-relativistic positively charged particle, in a uniform electric field E, will accelerate uniformly in the direction of the field, since

$$m \, \vec{a} = q \, \vec{E}. \tag{14-4}$$

According to this equation, the particle will accelerate indefinitely up to arbitrarily high velocities. A negatively charged particle accelerates in the opposite direction.

If only a uniform magnetic field is present,

$$m \, \vec{a} = q \, (\vec{v} \times \vec{B}), \tag{14-5}$$

so the acceleration is perpendicular to both the field and the velocity vector. A particle moving in the direction of the field is unaccelerated, since then $\vec{v} \times \vec{B} = 0$. But a particle moving perpendicular to the field accelerates in a direction perpendicular to both $\vec{v}$ and $\vec{B}$, resulting in circular motion at constant speed. The inward centripetal acceleration is

137

$$a = \frac{v^2}{r} = \frac{q}{m} v B \qquad (14\text{-}6)$$

so $mv = qBr$, or

$$p = qBr, \qquad (14\text{-}7)$$

where r is the radius of the orbit.

For <u>relativistic</u> particles $\vec{p} \neq m\vec{v}$, so $\frac{d\vec{p}}{dt} \neq m\vec{a}$. Therefore at least one of the equations

$$\vec{F} = m\vec{a} \text{ and } \vec{F} = \frac{d\vec{p}}{dt}$$

must be false for relativistic motion. Clearly, which (if either) is correct, depends upon what we choose to call <u>force</u>, and that, to some extent, is a matter of convenience. It is here that we fall back on electromagnetism and laboratory experience to guide us in this choice.

It is found experimentally that charged relativistic particles in electromagnetic fields move according to

$$\frac{d\vec{p}}{dt} = q (\vec{E} + \vec{v} \times \vec{B}) \qquad (14\text{-}8)$$

where $\vec{p}$ is the relativistic momentum $\vec{p} = \dfrac{m\vec{v}}{\sqrt{1 - v^2/c^2}}$.

It is therefore simple and natural to identify the Lorentz force $\vec{F} = q (\vec{E} + \vec{v} \times \vec{B})$ as the correct force for relativistic (as well as for non-relativistic) motion if the equation

$$\vec{F} = \frac{d\vec{p}}{dt} \qquad (14\text{-}9)$$

is used. The alternative possibility, $\vec{F} = m\vec{a}$, is therefore definitely <u>false</u> if we adopt the above force as a relativistic force.

As an example of relativistic motion, suppose a charge accelerates from rest in a uniform electric field. Then along the field direction $\frac{dp}{dt} = qE$, or $\dfrac{d}{dt} \dfrac{mv}{\sqrt{1 - v^2/c^2}} = \dfrac{m}{(1 - v^2/c^2)^{3/2}} \dfrac{dv}{dt} = q\,E$, carrying out the differentiation.

The acceleration is therefore

$$a = \frac{dv}{dt} = \frac{qE}{m}(1 - v^2/c^2)^{3/2} \tag{14-10}$$

showing that the acceleration decreases as $v \to c$, which is necessary in order to prevent the charge from reaching the speed of light. The equation can be integrated to give

$$\frac{qE}{m}t = \frac{qE}{m}\int_0^t dt = \int_0^v \frac{dv}{(1 - v^2/c^2)^{3/2}} = \frac{v}{\sqrt{1 - v^2/c^2}}$$

and then solved for the velocity:

$$v = \frac{q\,Et/m}{\sqrt{1 + (\frac{qEt}{mc})^2}}. \tag{14-11}$$

Note that as $t \to \infty$, the denominator approaches qEt/mc, so $v \to c$. As expected, the charge nears, but never quite attains, the speed of light. Since $v = \frac{dx}{dt}$, the equation can be integrated again:

$$x = \int_0^x dx = \int_0^t \frac{(qEt/m)\,dt}{\sqrt{1 + (\frac{qEt}{mc})^2}} = \frac{mc^2}{qE}\left(\sqrt{1 + (\frac{qEt}{mc})^2} - 1\right). \tag{14-12}$$

As $t \to \infty$, $x \to ct$, so the charge moves almost as far as a light-beam starting at the same time.

As another example of relativistic motion, suppose the electric field is turned off, and a uniform **magnetic** field turned on instead. Then the equation of motion becomes

$$\frac{d\vec{p}}{dt} = q\,(\vec{v} \times \vec{B}). \tag{14-13}$$

No acceleration takes place if $\vec{B}$ is parallel to $\vec{v}$, so suppose that $\vec{B}$ is perpendicular to $\vec{v}$, or in particular that $\vec{B}$ is in the z direction and that $\vec{v}$ is in the x direction. There is then no component of force in the z-direction, so the particle moves about in the x-y plane. It is still true in relativistic mechanics that the momentum and velocity of

139

a particle are parallel, so taking the vector dot product of $\vec{p}$ with the equation,

$$\vec{p} \cdot \frac{d\vec{p}}{dt} = q\vec{p} \cdot (\vec{v} \times \vec{B}) = 0 \text{ (since } \vec{p} \parallel \vec{v}). \tag{14-14}$$

But $\vec{p} \cdot \frac{d\vec{p}}{dt} = \frac{1}{2} \frac{d}{dt} p^2$, so we have found that p^2 remains constant, implying that the absolute magnitude of the momentum and velocity are constants. Therefore

$$\frac{d\vec{p}}{dt} = \frac{d}{dt} \frac{m\vec{v}}{\sqrt{1 - v^2/c^2}} = \frac{m}{\sqrt{1 - v^2/c^2}} \frac{d\vec{v}}{dt} = q(\vec{v} \times \vec{B}) \tag{14-15}$$

using $\frac{d}{dt} v^2 = 0$. The acceleration $d\vec{v}/dt$ is perpendicular to the velocity, so the motion is circular. The centripetal acceleration for circular motion is $a = v^2/r$, so $\dfrac{m}{\sqrt{1 - v^2/c^2}} \dfrac{v^2}{r} = qvB,$

$$\text{or } p = qBr \tag{14-16}$$

— the same equation as for non-relativistic motion, except that now $p = \dfrac{mv}{\sqrt{1 - v^2/c^2}}$. The angular frequency is

$$\omega = \frac{v}{r} = \frac{qB}{m} \sqrt{1 - v^2/c^2} \ , \tag{14-17}$$

showing that unlike the situation with non-relativistic motion, the relativistic angular frequency depends upon the velocity of the particle. This fact is used in the design of high-energy cyclotrons, and is well verified experimentally.

In non-relativistic mechanics, the power transferred to a particle by a force $\vec{F}$ shows up as an increasing particle energy:

$$\vec{F} \cdot \vec{v} = dE/dt. \tag{14-18}$$

It is easy to prove that the same equation holds true for relativistic motion. Since the relativistic relation between energy and momentum is

$$E^2 = \vec{p}^2 c^2 + m^2 c^4, \tag{9-13}$$

differentiation gives $2E \frac{dE}{dt} = 2 \vec{p} c^2 \cdot \frac{\vec{dp}}{dt}$. But $\frac{\vec{pc}^2}{E} = \vec{v}$, so

$\frac{dE}{dt} = \vec{v} \cdot \frac{\vec{dp}}{dt} = \vec{v} \cdot \vec{F}$ which is identical with the non-relativistic relation

(14-18). An electric field $\vec{E}$ injects energy into a charged particle

at a rate $q \vec{v} \cdot \vec{E}$. But since the magnetic force $q (\vec{v} \times \vec{B})$ is always

perpendicular to the velocity vector $\vec{v}$, the rate at which work is done

by a magnetic field, $q\vec{v} \cdot (\vec{v} \times \vec{B})$, is always identically zero. This of

course is consistent with the special example of a particle moving

perpendicular to a uniform magnetic field, where the speed doesn't

change.

The relativistic equation of motion $\vec{F} = \frac{\vec{dp}}{dt}$ has been justified by its

agreement with experiment in the case of the simple Lorentz force

$\vec{F} = q(\vec{E} + \vec{v} \times \vec{B})$. This may seem restrictive, and not an indication

of the general validity of the equation. However, the equation is some-

what more general than it may seem. There are many forces, including

most familiar forces, which are actually complicated sums of simple

Lorentz forces. For example, the force of a spring consists of the sum

of many atomic forces, each electrical in nature. Each atom contributes

a force and causes a momentum change, and they all together produce a

total force and cause a total momentum change, still related by $\vec{F} = \frac{\vec{dp}}{dt}$.

Besides electromagnetism, only three other fundamental forces are

known. These are the strong (nuclear) force, the weak force (causing

the β-decay of nuclei and the decay of many elementary particles), and

gravitation. The strong and weak forces occur in situations where

quantum mechanics must be used, so no classical-type equation like

$\vec{F} = \frac{\vec{dp}}{dt}$ could be used for these forces. If Einstein's general theory of

relativity is correct, gravity is a consequence of the curvature of space-

time, and isn't even a force at all! In this theory, massive particles

move in such a way as to maximize their proper time between two given

positions, which Einstein showed was equivalent to an equation of motion

rather similar to $\vec{F} = \frac{\vec{dp}}{dt}$, but more complicated.

Lorentz forces and the relativistic equation of motion are important in a

variety of applications, and particularly in the design and operation of high-energy particle accelerators. In machines such as electron linear accelerators or proton synchrotrons, the accelerated particles move at nearly the speed of light, so the use of the relativistic equation of motion is essential. In these machines, and in the collisions of fundamental particles which they are built to study, relativistic dynamics is tested daily.

Einstein's two simple postulates have indeed been revolutionary. In this book, we have only barely begun to look at physics from a relativistic point of view; we have only begun to take the idea of spacetime seriously. We have not taken a major step into relativistic electromagnetism, nor have we shown how relativity and quantum mechanics can be combined. We've only begun.

PROBLEMS XIV

1. An idealized Van de Graaff electrostatic accelerator maintains a uniform electric field of $E = 10^5$ volts/meter over a distance of ten meters.

    (a) From Eq. 14-11 and 14-12, find the velocity of an electron which accelerates through the ten meters.

    (b) From the information given, we would expect the final kinetic energy of the electron to be 1 Mev. Verify this by using the result of part (a), along with the definition of relativistic kinetic energy.

2. A spaceship of mass 10^6 kilograms is subjected to a constant force F as measured in a fixed inertial frame of reference. If this ship is supposed to reach the star Alpha Centauri (4-1/3 light-years away) in ten years (as measured in the fixed inertial frame), find find

    (a) the force F;

    (b) the ship's kinetic energy when it reaches Alpha Centauri;

    (c) the power input to the ship when it reaches Alpha Centauri.

3. A beam of 500 Mev (kinetic energy) positive pi-mesons shoots into a bending magnet which maintains a magnetic field B = 2.0 webers/ meter^2 (which are MKS units) perpendicular to the beam. If the pions are in the field for a distance of 20 centimeters, through what angle are they deflected by the magnet?

GENERAL BIBLIOGRAPHY

1. A. Einstein, H. A. Lorentz, H. Minkowski, and H. Weyl, The Principle of Relativity, (Dover Publications, 1923). Reprints of original articles.

2. A. Einstein, The Meaning of Relativity, (Princeton University Press, 1955). An advanced book which includes general relativity.

3. P. A. Schilpp (editor), Albert Einstein: Philosopher-Scientist, (Harper Torch books, 1959). Contains autobiographical notes by Einstein.

4. W. Pauli, Theory of Relativity, (Pergamon Press, 1958).

5. C. Møller, The Theory of Relativity (Oxford University Press, 1952).

6. P. G. Bergmann, Introduction to the Theory of Relativity (Prentice-Hall, 1942).

7. M. Born, Einstein's Theory of Relativity, (Dover Productions, 1962).

8. D. Bohm, The Special Theory of Relativity, (Benjamin, 1965).

9. G. Holton, "Resource Letter SRT-1 on Special Relativity Theory" in the Am. Jour. of Phys. 30, 462 (1962). This article contains references to many others.

APPENDIX A
RIGID BODIES

ONE OF THE MOST CONVENIENT notions in classical mechanics is
that of a rigid body. A rigid body is simply an object where the distance
between any two particles in the object always remains the same; it
doesn't bend, twist, or stretch, but moves as a unit. For many purposes we can treat a rigid body as though it were a single particle, lo-
calized at the center-of-mass, and having a fixed moment of inertia.

Now it is evident that there is really no such thing in nature as a rigid
body, because nothing is infinitely "stiff." Every real object can bend
and twist to some extent, so that for example when you spin it, it will
stretch slightly, causing the moment of inertia to increase. Nevertheless in many cases these effects are <u>small</u>, so that the rigid body ap-
proximation is pretty good, and of course very useful.

Special relativity now enters the picture, telling us that not even <u>in</u>
<u>principle</u> can a perfectly rigid body exist. Because all signals travel
with only finite speed ($< c$), no object can be completely stiff. For
example, if one end of a steel bar is struck with a hammer, the other
end of the bar can't possibly feel the blow immediately. Thus one end
of the bar may begin to move while the other end remains at rest, because the signal hasn't yet had time to propagate from one end to the
other. So this object is not a rigid body at all. It cannot be described
as a single particle.

This inherent lack of rigidity is a help in understanding some so-called
"paradoxes" in the relativity theory. One such puzzle will be posed
here, as originally invented by E. M. Dewan, [*] and left for the reader
to resolve. It is worth thinking about not only because it casts light
on the "rigid body" notion, but also because it graphically demonstrates
the fact that the simultaneity of two events is a relative concept, depending on the observer.

---

[*] <u>Am. Jour. of Phys.</u> <u>31</u>, 383 (1963).

The paradox begins on a farm. On the farm is a smallish barn which has a front door which can be opened and closed, and a rear wall which is unusually sturdy. A friend of ours, a pole-vaulter, owns a pole which is exactly twice as long as the barn, so that it can't fit inside. The pole-vaulter has the virtue of being extremely speedy, so we request that he walk quite a distance away from the barn, and then (with his pole in a horizontal position) run toward the barn as shown in Figure A.1. The front door of the barn opens inward, so we open the door, but stand behind it inside. Our friend then runs quickly toward the barn, fast enough so that from our point of view the pole has contracted by better than a factor of two. So he runs into the barn with his contracted pole, at which point we slam the front door shut, thereby capturing him inside the barn with a pole which isn't supposed to fit!

Since the rear wall of the barn is very sturdy, he is brought to a halt, but as he stops his contracted pole expands back to its full size. The only outcome then is for the expanded pole to shove the pole-vaulter back through the closed front door, perhaps knocking out part of the front wall as well!

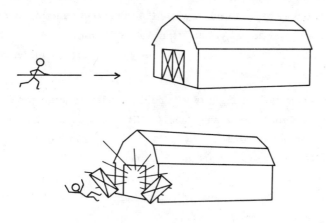

Figure A.1

The puzzle arises if we try to consider this series of events from the standpoint of the pole vaulter. To him, the pole retains its full length,

146

but it is the <u>barn</u> which has shrunk by better than half. So it would seem absolutely impossible for the pole and himself to get into the barn. Yet <u>we</u> saw him in the barn, and he knocked out the front wall on his way back out! The barn has been partially demolished from anyone's point of view! So what happened to the pole vaulter as he himself saw it?

APPENDIX B
RELATIVISTIC MASS

IT HAS BEEN COMMON, in presenting the theory of relativity, to speak of the so-called "relativistic mass," defined by the equation

$$m_R = \frac{m_o}{\sqrt{1 - v^2/c^2}} \; ,$$

where m_o is the ordinary "rest-mass" of the particle (denoted simply by "m" in this book). This equation leads to statements like "mass increases with velocity" and "nothing can reach the speed of light because then its mass would be infinite." Because the idea of relativistic mass is so widespread, and because in some ways the idea is useful, it is necessary to discuss its meaning. It is not used anywhere in this book, because it was felt that the disadvantages of using relativistic mass outweigh the advantages. We will attempt to explain how the notion of relativistic mass arises, what it means physically, and what its advantages and disadvantages are as a way of describing relativistic particles.

We have shown that the correct expression for the momentum of a particle is

$$\vec{p} = \frac{m\vec{v}}{\sqrt{1 - v^2/c^2}} \; .$$

This definition of momentum came from trying to find a quantity $\vec{p}$ which is conserved in collisions and which reduces to the classical expression $\vec{p} = m\vec{v}$ for low velocities. Suppose however that we wanted to retain in relativistic mechanics the classical form $\vec{p} = m\vec{v}$ for momentum. Then clearly we are going to have to say $\vec{p} = m_R\vec{v}$, where $m_R = \dfrac{m}{\sqrt{1 - v^2/c^2}}$ is a velocity-dependent "relativistic mass." This is one place where the notion of relativistic mass comes from — by trying to retain the equation $\vec{p} = m\vec{v}$.

Some of the <u>advantages</u> of using relativistic mass are:

148

1. There is a simple form for the momentum $\vec{p} = m_R \vec{v}$.
2. There is a simple form for the <u>total energy</u>: $E = m_R c^2$.
3. It gives a simple intuitive reason for the increased inertia or "sluggishness" of objects at high velocity: they are more massive so it is harder to make them go faster.

Some of the <u>disadvantages</u> of using relativistic mass are:

1. By hiding $\sqrt{1 - v^2/c^2}$ in the mass, we may forget it is there. It is safer to exhibit explicitly in the formulas all such factors, by writing

$$\vec{p} = \frac{m\vec{v}}{\sqrt{1 - v^2/c^2}} = \gamma m\vec{v}, \text{ and } E = \frac{mc^2}{\sqrt{1 - v^2/c^2}} = \gamma mc^2.$$

2. One may get the mistaken impression that to go from classical to relativistic mechanics it is only necessary to replace all masses by m_R. This certainly works for the momentum $\vec{p} = m\vec{v}$, but it <u>does not</u> work, for example, for kinetic energy: $1/2\, m_R v^2 \neq$ relativistic energy.

Calling $1/2\, m_R v^2 = 1/2\, \dfrac{mv^2}{\sqrt{1 - v^2/c^2}}$ the relativistic kinetic energy is a common error, brought about partly by the idea of relativistic mass.

3. Relativity fundamentally serves to correct our notions about <u>time</u> and <u>space</u>. Thus it is really the <u>dynamical</u> quantities dealing with motion, like velocity and momentum, which ought to be changed, and not the properties of individual particles (like mass).

4. When relativity is put in four-dimensional form, as in Chapter XIII, the idea of relativistic mass is out of place and clumsy.

In any event, as long as the equations are really the <u>same</u>, we can use ordinary or relativistic mass, and no physics will be changed. One person will choose to use $\vec{p} = \dfrac{m\vec{v}}{\sqrt{1 - v^2/c^2}}$, and someone else will use $\vec{p} = m_R \vec{v}$, but since these are identical equations, all results calculated from them will be the same. The reader can judge whether he wants to use relativistic mass or not, from the advantages and disadvantages listed, and from experience in thinking about relativity.

APPENDIX C
THE APPEARANCE OF MOVING OBJECTS

THE LORENTZ-FITZGERALD CONTRACTION was discussed in Chapter V, and it was concluded that it is essential, in measuring the length of a moving body, to measure the position of the two ends simultaneously. Any other kind of measurement would fail to correspond to our usual definition of length. Obviously, measuring the position of one end at one time, and the other end at a different time, would be a poor definition. Yet it is just this kind of measurement which is being made when a single observer watches a moving object, or when a snapshot is taken. A snapshot of a moving train won't necessarily record its "true" length, since photons will generally have left different parts of the train at different times. Thus a snapshot made of a train traveling on a track running past us will make the train appear longer during its approach, and shorter during its departure. This effect is just a consequence of the finite speed of light, and should not be blamed on the theory of relativity.

A detailed study of how a moving three-dimensional object would appear to a single observer (or on a snapshot) was carried out for the first time in 1959, by J. L. Terrell.[*] We have thought of a train as a one-dimensional object having an apparent length depending on its speed and position, but the visual appearance of three-dimensional objects wasn't discussed. The result is somewhat surprising. It turns out that if an observer watches a moving object, that object will appear to be rotated.

A convenient three-dimensional object to look at is a cubical block of wood with lettered sides for purposes of identification, as in Figure C.1. Two views of the block are shown. We suppose that this block moves past us from left to right at high speed, so that side B is parallel to the track and faces us just as the block goes by. If we don't think very carefully, we might think the process would look as shown

---

[*] J. L. Terrell, Phys. Rev. 116, 1041, 1959.

in Figure C.2. (The figure
shows five views of the block
as it approaches, passes, and
recedes.) The block is shown
stretched out as it approaches,
Lorentz-contracted as it pas-

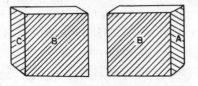

Figure C.1

ses by, and compressed as it leaves. But in fact the block will **actually**
look as shown in Figure C.3! It will not appear to be distorted, but
rather it will look like an ordinary cubical block which has been rotated.
As it approaches, it suffers an apparent partial twist, so that somewhere

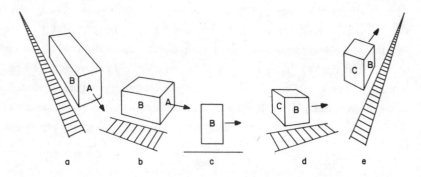

Figure C.2

between views a and b we see only side B. Then in picture b we
have entirely lost side A, which is supposed to be toward us, and are
beginning to see side C, which is supposed to be away from us. This
twist persists as the block passes by, but becomes less pronounced as
the block leaves.

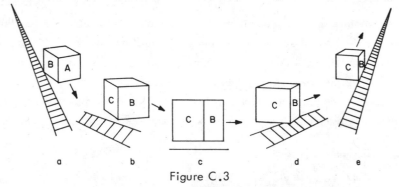

Figure C.3

152

The twist effect can be understood by studying the series of constructions in Figure C.4. The basic idea is that if the block is moving very fast (v = .9c in Figure C.4), the block can get out of the way of the light from side C as long as the light moves at a sufficiently great angle with respect to the direction of motion of the block. Similarly, the block tends to "run into" the light from side A, thus causing it to disappear by the time the block reaches position b. As an example of how the constructions were made, consider Figure C.4a. The block, which would be cubical when at rest, has been contracted in its direction of motion by the factor

$$\sqrt{1 - v^2/c^2} = \sqrt{1 - .9^2} = .436.$$

Suppose light leaves corner 1 of the block and moves toward an observer at the lower right in the direction shown. We assume the observer is far away compared to the size of the block, so that all the light he intercepts will be moving in parallel paths. Then the distances w, x, y, and z are constructed so that

$$x = \frac{V}{c} z = .9z, \text{ and } w = \frac{V}{c} y = .9y$$

which insures that the light from corners 2 and 3 will reach the observer at the same time as corner 1. That is, when the observer sees the original light from corner 1, he will see corner 3 when the block is a distance w to the right, and he will see corner 2 when it is a distance x to the right. The block then appears to the observer as shown in construction 1. Side B looks wider than you might expect, while side C looks narrower. Construction 2 shows that the net effect is as though the observer were watching a rotated stationary block.

The reason why the visual appearance of a moving block is identical to that of a rotated block is most easily understood when the block is at its closest position to us. Normally in this position we would expect to see only side B, contracted by the factor $\sqrt{1 - v^2/c^2}$. But actually side C can also be seen in this position because the block moves out of the way of the light being emitted from that side, allowing us to see it.

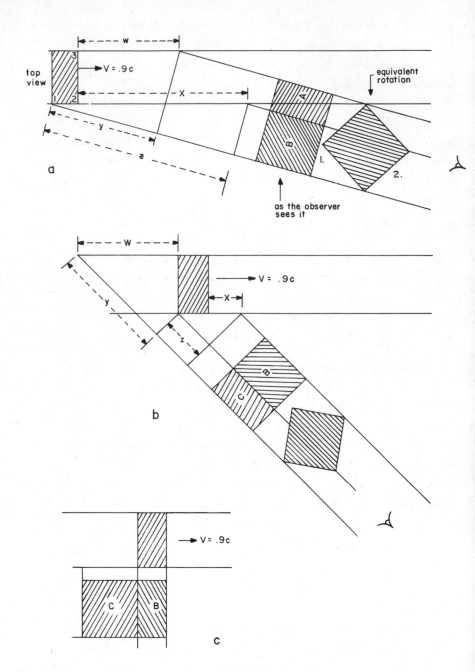

Figure C.4

154

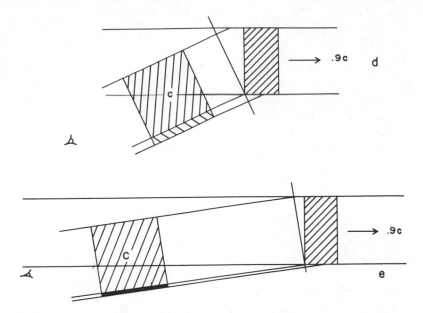

Figure C.4 (continued)

The light from the <u>back</u> edge of side C had to be emitted earlier than the light from the <u>front</u> edge in order for it to reach our eye at the same time. Figure C.5 shows that the apparent width of side C is v/c meters. Therefore the block will appear as in Figure C.5a. Figure C.5b shows a similar block, stationary but rotated. The view of this object is the <u>same</u> as that of the fast-moving but unrotated block.

Other objects also look rotated, so that for example a sphere will always look spherical, and will <u>not</u> appear to the eye to be squashed in its direction of motion. To be precise, we should say that the exactly rotated appearance only holds good when the object subtends a small angle at our eye. Large nearby objects will be distorted, and the analysis is more complicated.

It is interesting that since the sun and moon move with respect to us, the twist effect makes them appear rotated from their actual position. It is straightforward to show that the rotation angle $\Delta \theta$ is given by

$$\cos \Delta \theta = \sqrt{1 - v^2/c^2}$$

155

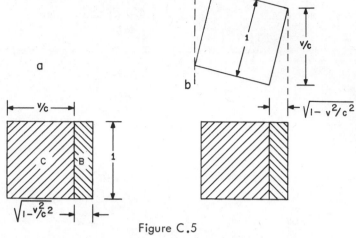

Figure C.5

where v is the relative (sideways) velocity of the object and us. This rotation angle can be used to find out how much of the object is hidden and how much is uncovered due to the twist effect, and the result is worth working out!

REFERENCES

1. The original paper on the visual appearance of moving objects is by J. Terrell, "Invisibility of the Lorentz Contraction," Phys. Rev. 116, 1041 (1959).

2. An excellent pictorial discussion is given by V. F. Weisskopf, in "The Visual Appearance of Rapidly Moving Objects," Physics Today 13, 24 (1960).

APPENDIX D

GRAVITATION AND THE PRINCIPLE OF EQUIVALENCE

EINSTEIN'S THEORY OF SPECIAL RELATIVITY is very powerful in
scope, because it has things to say about the foundations on which
physics is built. All of physics must be carefully scrutinized to see
if it conforms to relativistic requirements. Thus the electromagnetism
of Maxwell was found to pass the test, and was actually partially justified and strengthened by the relativistic point of view. On the other
hand, classical mechanics had to be revised in order to satisfy
Einstein's demand that the fundamental laws be invariant under the
Lorentz Transformation. Here we examine Newton's law of gravitational attraction, summarized by the central force

$$F = \frac{Gmm'}{r^2} \tag{D-1}$$

which varies as the product of the two masses involved and inversely
as the square of the distance between them. We would like to know if
this law passes the test of relativity, or if instead a new theory of
gravity is required.

The questioning of Newtonian gravitation at first seems unnecessary
or even arrogant, since calculations made on planetary motion using
Newton's formula agree with experiment to a very high degree of accuracy. In fact two planets were discovered by the deviations they
caused in the calculated orbits of other planets. Yet from a relativistic
point of view, Newton's law of gravitation cannot be correct as it
stands, but needs at least a partial modification!

First of all, how should one interpret the distance r between two
masses? Who is supposed to measure this distance? Since lengths
have lost their absolute character in relativity, an observer on one
mass may measure a different distance than an observer on the other
mass. We have no reasonable way to specify what distance should be
used! It is also implied in the formula that if you want to know the
force between two objects now, you should put in the "distance between

157

them" <u>now</u>. But how does one mass know where the other mass is now?
If no signal can travel with infinite speed, a given mass can only feel
where another was at an earlier time — at least the time it takes light to
travel between them.

Another interesting comment one could make about Newton's formula is
that the force depends on the particle <u>masses</u>. Yet in relativity theory
mass is just one form of energy. Why should gravity act only on that
part of the energy contained in mass? Might it not also act upon (and
be caused by) kinetic energy and massless particles like photons?

Finally, there is a fact about gravitation which doesn't disagree with
Newton's theory, but which isn't explained by it either. That is the fact
that in writing the equation of motion of a particle in a gravitational field,
the mass of the particle cancels out, and so does not influence the motion. This of course is just "Galileo's experiment" of dropping two different masses and noticing that they accelerate equally. The mass m
in the force law $\dfrac{G\,m\,m'}{r^2}$ we could call the <u>gravitational</u> mass, whereas
the mass m in the "inertial-force" $m\,\vec{a}$ could be called <u>inertial</u> mass.
The fact that these masses are equal, or at least proportional through
the constant G, is not explained in Newton's theory of gravity.

For these and other reasons, after completing special relativity
Einstein went to work on a new theory of gravitation. This led to his
general theory of relativity, published in 1915. The theory overcomes
the objections to Newton's theory, and also has the required property
that it reduce to special relativity in the absence of masses, and that
it reduce to Newton's gravitation for non-relativistic objects in weak
fields. Einstein's <u>special</u> relativity was the result of carefully developing the idea that light moves at the same velocity in all frames.
An equally simple but powerful idea, which he called the "Principle of
Equivalence, " guided him in the construction of <u>general</u> relativity.
By using this principle, along with some beautiful mathematics describing curved space as invented by Gauss, Riemann, and others, Einstein
proposed a theory of gravity which accounts for gravitational phenomena
in terms of a curved "non-Euclidean" geometry of space-time. Although

a retracing of the general theory is far beyond the scope of this book, the equivalence principle by itself leads to some interesting results. We discuss it here for its own interest and because it is useful in understanding the twin paradox, as taken up in Appendix E.

There are several ways to state the principle of equivalence, some of which are not equivalent to others! The reader is referred to the references for all but the single approach we take here. Imagine two spaceships, one of which is uniformly accelerating in empty space without any gravitational field, and the other standing at rest in a uniform gravitational field, as shown in Figure D.1. The principle of equivalence then claims that an experiment performed inside the accelerating ship will give the same result as an exactly similar experiment inside the ship at rest in the uniform field.

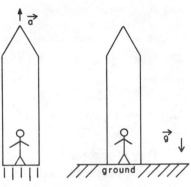

Figure D.1

A key word here is "inside," since you could clearly distinguish between the two situations by looking outside to see if you are standing on some large mass or not. The principle is a way of expressing the observed fact that inertial and gravitational mass are equal. In the accelerating ship, it is an inside observer's <u>inertial</u> mass which "causes" him to press against the floor; in the stationary ship it is his <u>gravitational</u> mass which performs this function. The equivalence of these two situations is quite reasonable for mechanics: intuition and exact analysis agree that the motion of an object inside is the same in either case. What is not so clear is that the principle applies to experiments with electricity, light, atomic and nuclear physics as well as mechanics. Yet Einstein decided to pursue this principle, supposing it to be universally valid, to see where it would lead him. We will use the principle here to deduce two effects of gravity which aren't contained in Newton's theory: the effect of gravitational potential on the rate of clocks, and the bending

159

of light in a uniform field. These effects are deduced by considering two experiments with light waves.

The first application of the equivalence principle to the behavior of light waves is the derivation of the so-called "gravitational red-shift." This phenomenon can be understood as an influence of gravitation on the rate of clocks, quite apart from the special relativity effects met with earlier. To derive this effect, we make use of the device of deducing the result of an experiment performed in a uniformly accelerating rocket, and then claim by virtue of the equivalence principle that the experiment would give the same result in a rocket at rest in a uniform gravitational field. The "experiment" is simple in principle, but would be difficult to carry out in practice.

At the top of the accelerating rocket is an observer who shines a flashlight at another observer at the bottom of the rocket, as shown in Figure D.2. For simplicity we assume the flashlight emits monochromatic light, and also that the distance traveled by the bottom observer while the light comes to him is small compared to the length of the ship. It follows that the time it takes for the light to reach him is about $t = \ell/c$, where ℓ is the distance between the two observers. But during this time the bottom observer has attained a velocity $v = at = a\ell/c$ with respect to the velocity of the flashlight when the light was emitted. He is moving toward the source, so he will observe a blue-shift due to the Doppler effect. Since we have already assumed his velocity is small, so as to neglect the distance he travels compared to the distance ℓ, we can use the non-relativistic Doppler formula to give

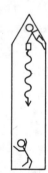

Figure D.2

$$\nu_{observed} = \nu_{emitted}\,(1 + v/c) = \nu_{emitted}\,(1 + a\ell/c^2). \qquad (D-2)$$

160

Clearly if instead the bottom observer were to shine a monochromatic flashlight at the top observer, the top observer would observe a red-shift, since by the time he received the light he would be moving away from where the source was when the light was emitted.

Now by means of the equivalence principle we can claim that the same effects would be observed in a rocket at rest in a uniform gravitational field, if we substitute the acceleration of gravity g for the rocket acceleration a. That is, if the observer at the top of the ship were to shine a frequency $\nu_{emitted}$ toward the lower observer, the lower observer would see a frequency $\nu_{observed} = \nu_{emitted} (1+g\ell/c^2)$, a blue-shift, whereas the top observer would see a red-shift if he looked at a light beam sent off by the lower observer. But in this case we can hardly blame the shift on Doppler, because neither observer is moving. We have to invoke some other explanation to understand the change in frequency in a rocket at rest in a uniform field. This situation is reminiscent of the muon decay problem of Chapters IV and V, where it was necessary to explain why the muons failed to decay before they had penetrated the atmosphere. The fact of penetration held in both the earth and muon frames, but the reason for the fact was different in the two frames. Observers on the earth explained it by saying that the muon clocks ran slow, whereas the muon explained it by saying that the atmosphere was thin because of the Lorentz contraction.

How then can we explain the blue-shift seen by the man at the bottom of the stationary rocket? If we think of the atoms which radiate the light as clocks whose rate is indicated by the frequency of their emitted light, the observer at the bottom would be forced to conclude that these clocks are running fast compared to similar clocks beside him. His own clocks radiate a certain frequency, while atoms higher up radiate a higher frequency. The observer at the top would agree with his judgment. He sees a red-shift when he looks at atoms below him, so he would say that his own clocks are running faster than those below him.

If atomic clocks up high run faster, it is of course true that all clocks up high run faster. For suppose a clock at the top of the rocket has a luminous second-hand emitting light of frequency $\nu = 5 \times 10^{14} \text{ sec}^{-1}$, corresponding to a yellow color. Then in one complete revolution of the second-hand $60 \times 5 \times 10^{14} = 3 \times 10^{16}$ waves will be emitted. The observer at the bottom must also see 3×10^{16} waves/ revolution, since none are created or destroyed in transmission. But the frequency of the waves would increase by the factor $(1+g\ell/c^2)$, so it follows that the second-hand of the clock at the top appears to complete a revolution in less than 60 seconds to the man at the bottom, by the exact same factor.

The gravitational effect on clock rates is not so paradoxical as the time-dilation effect for moving clocks, since both the upper and lower observers agree that the upper clocks run faster than the lower clocks. It is interesting that the quantity $g\ell$ is just the difference in gravitational potential $\Delta\phi$, in a uniform field. In terms of $\Delta\phi$, the potential energy $(mg\ell)$ of a particle having mass m is $m\Delta\phi$. The gravitational effect on clocks can therefore be written

$$\nu_{observed} = \nu_{emitted} \, (1 + \Delta\phi/c^2) \qquad\qquad \text{(D-3)}$$

where the sign of $\Delta\phi$ is chosen to make light from higher clocks have a higher frequency.

It is easy to calculate the magnitude of this effect on the earth's surface. Using a uniform g of about 9.8 m/sec^2, a clock on top of 29,028-foot Mt. Everest would run faster than a similar clock at sea level by about one part in 10^{12}, which amounts to a gain of one second in 30,000 years. Within the past few years it has become feasible to perform experiments of this accuracy, using the Mössbauer effect, which allows an extremely sensitive determination of frequency changes in γ-ray photons. This effect was used by Pound and Rebka[*] in 1960 to measure the gravitational effect on the frequency of 14.4 kilovolt photons emitted by the isotope Fe^{57}. They used a tower 74 feet high, for which we would calculate a shift of $\Delta\nu/\nu = g\ell/c^2 = 2.5 \times 10^{-15}$. They observed a shift, and found that

---

[*] Pound and Rebka, Phys. Rev. Letters 4, 337, 1960

$$\frac{\Delta\nu \text{ experiment}}{\Delta\nu \text{ theory}} = (1.05 \pm .10),$$

which is excellent agreement, especially considering that the experiment was so delicate that a 1° temperature difference between the top and bottom of the tower would have destroyed the effect, due to Doppler shifts caused by different velocities of the nuclei in the two positions.

If we assume that the factor $1 + \Delta\phi/c^2$ is also valid for non-uniform fields, for which $\Delta\phi \neq g\ell$, the frequency shift of light from the sun and stars can be used to test the theory. The change in potential energy in going from the surface of the sun to the surface of the earth is

$$\Delta\phi = -\frac{G\,M_{sun}}{R_{sun}} + \frac{G\,M_{earth}}{R_{earth}} .$$

The second term is much smaller than the first, so the frequency shift is:

$$\frac{\Delta\nu}{\nu_{emitted}} = \frac{\nu_{observed} - \nu_{emitted}}{\nu_{emitted}} \cong -\frac{G\,M_{sun}}{R_{sun}c^2} \cong -2 \times 10^{-6} ,$$

or a red-shift of two parts per million. White dwarf stars, with nearly the sun's mass compressed to the size of the earth, have a red-shift about 100 times as large. Shifts have been observed from both the sun and white dwarfs, and are in agreement with the theory, although there is considerable error due to other causes of line-shifting. The shifts are found, of course, by comparing observed atomic spectra with spectra from laboratory sources.

A second application of the equivalence principle is the calculation of the bending of light in a gravitational field. In this experiment, a flashlight is aimed sideways in each rocket, as shown in Figure D.3. We can analyze the motion of the light beam in the accelerating ship, and then claim the results must be the same in the rocket at rest in a uniform field. Making again the assumption that the acceleration is small enough so the rocket doesn't attain relativistic velocities while the light travels from left to right, we know that if the light takes time t to cross the ship, the ship will have moved a distance $\frac{1}{2}$ at t^2.

Therefore, although the light beam moves in a straight line as seen by inertial observers, it moves in a curved parabolic path as seen by observers on the accelerating ship. If x and y are the horizontal and vertical distances covered by the beam, $x = ct$ and $y = \frac{1}{2} at^2$, giving $y = \frac{a}{2c^2} x^2$. By the equivalence principle, we can then say that

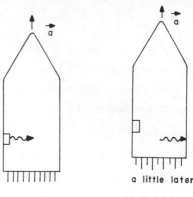

a little later

Figure D.3

light will fall a distance $y = \frac{g}{2c^2} x^2$ in a uniform gravitational field as well. This prediction is even harder to verify than the red-shift phenomenon. A light beam aimed sideways along the earth's surface would fall a distance $\frac{9.8}{2 \cdot 9 \cdot 10^{16}} \cdot 1000^2 = .54 \times 10^{-10}$ meters for every 1000 meters of horizontal travel. This distance is about the radius of a hydrogen atom.

The deflection of the light of a star around the sun during a total eclipse has been seen, although it is quite small. Since the gravitational field of the sun is not uniform, it is necessary to work out how much light bends around a spherical object. Using his general theory of relativity, Einstein computed the deflection around the sun to be 1.75 seconds of arc. The experiments show a wide degree of scatter, but are at least not in serious disagreement with Einstein's value. General relativity hasn't had the same thorough and wide-ranging experimental verification enjoyed by special relativity, since the experiments in question are so difficult. New experiments are gradually becoming technically feasible, so we can hope for some clarification in the future.

REFERENCE

1. The books by Einstein and several other books listed in the general bibliography contain discussions of the equivalence principle and general relativity.

APPENDIX E

THE TWIN PARADOX

AS MENTIONED IN Chapter IV, the time-dilation effect can lead to apparently paradoxical conclusions. For each of two relatively moving inertial observers to claim that the other observer's clock runs slow seems contradictory and nonsensical. Nevertheless, as illustrated in section D of Chapter VI, there is actually no contradiction. When account is taken of the Lorentz contraction and the fact that two clocks in one frame are not synchronized when viewed from another frame, the "paradox" is resolved. In that section on "Rockets and Clocks, " only inertial clocks and inertial observers were considered. No clocks or observers were accelerated during any portion of the experiment. Therefore that discussion has no bearing on the consistency of the twin story, in which one twin departs for Sirius and returns, necessarily accelerating during at least part of the trip. In order to understand this situation from both points of view, it is necessary to know how to deal with accelerating clocks and accelerating observers.

As pointed out several times in the text, special relativity deals only with observations made by inertial observers. Therefore the twin who accelerates cannot use the Lorentz transformation or any deductions from it, such as time dilation or length contraction. This should not be construed as a claim that special relativity can't be used to analyze accelerating objects, including rods and clocks. As long as the acceleration, momentum, energy, and other properties of a particle are measured by inertial observers, the transformations of special relativity can be used to calculate these quantities in any other inertial frame.

Thus our first project in this appendix is a discussion of accelerating clocks, so that the twin who stays at home can calculate the aging of the traveling twin while that twin is accelerating. Secondly, in order to analyze events from the viewpoint of the traveler, we have to know how clocks behave when viewed from accelerating frames of reference.

Neither of these two projects is simple. A thorough analysis of accelerating frames of reference must be reserved for a study of

165

Einstein's general theory of relativity. We will do here as much as we can with the results of Appendix D, coming from the principle of equivalence. Even the topic of accelerating clocks viewed from inertial frames will involve here a number of assumptions.

With regard to accelerating clocks, we'll assume all our clocks are "ideal." Such a clock is not affected by acceleration per se, but simply runs slow by the time-dilation factor $\sqrt{1 - v^2/c^2}$ appropriate for the velocity it has at each moment. There is probably no real clock which is completely ideal, since an acceleration would likely have some effect on any clock we might devise. As an extreme example, a watch which decelerates as it hits the floor may have its rate drastically altered. Similarly, the traveling twin would not want to accelerate too fast as he leaves for Sirius. An atomic or nuclear clock, whose rate is measured by the frequency of emitted radiation, is a nearly ideal clock for reasonable accelerations. Certainly for the accelerations likely to occur in spaceships, such a clock could be considered ideal. Of course any other kind of clock could be used if it were near enough to ideal, or if it could be corrected for the effects of acceleration.

Assuming that we have such a clock, we would like to know what it reads as compared with a similar clock at rest in an inertial frame. During an infinitesimal time interval dt (as measured by the inertial clock) the accelerating clock will have some velocity v, so will record a time interval $d\tau = dt \sqrt{1 - v^2/c^2}$ due to time dilation. Since the velocity depends on time, this expression has to be integrated for finite time intervals. If we choose $\tau = 0$ when $t = 0$, then the time read by the accelerating clock is

$$\tau = \int_{0}^{t} dt \sqrt{1 - v^2/c^2}, \qquad \text{(E-1)}$$

which is called the "integrated proper time."

Regarding accelerating observers and their measurement of clock rates, it was found in Appendix D that clocks run at different rates at different points in an accelerating frame. The effect could be understood as a gravitational influence on clocks, with those at high altitudes running faster than those at lower altitudes. To first-order accuracy, the ratio of the rates of two clocks is $(1+g\ell/c^2)$, where g is the (uniform) acceleration or gravitational field, and ℓ is the difference in altitude. It is important to note that it is the gravitational potential rather than the gravitational force itself which influences this rate.

We have now assembled the machinery needed to tackle the story of the twins to first-order accuracy from the point of view of both twins. We will find that the relative youthfulness of the traveling twin upon his return is a consistent result, agreed upon by both. An exact analysis confirms this consistency in detail, but is considerably more difficult to carry out, principally because of the need for careful definitions of coordinates and clock rates in accelerating frames. An exact treatment can be found in Møller's book. [*] The first-order analysis we will do here has the advantage of simplicity and displays the main features of the complete treatment. Throughout the following, all times will refer to the readings of ideal clocks.

The situation is, then, as follows: twin A stays at home, remaining in an inertial frame at all times. Twin B accelerates away, coasts toward Sirius, decelerates to rest, accelerates back, coasts toward the earth, and decelerates and stops, all as shown in Figure E.1. We may as well assume that the trip is symmetrical, so that all the acceleration and deceleration times are of equal duration as read by clocks in A's frame, say $\Delta t_1^{(A)}$, and that the going and coming coast periods have the same velocity and duration $\Delta t_2^{(A)}$. With this introduction we can now calculate the total time interval read by both clocks, first from A's point of view, and then from B's point of view.

To A:

The total time read by A's clock between B's departure and return is

$$\Delta T^{(A)} = 4\Delta t_1^{(A)} + 2\Delta t_2^{(A)}, \tag{E-2}$$

---

[*] C. Møller. The Theory of Relativity (Oxford University Press, 1952)

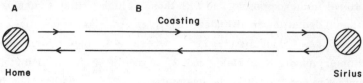

A   B   Coasting

Home   Sirius

Figure E.1

since there are four acceleration periods and two coasting periods. Now the ratio $\Delta t_1^{(A)}/\Delta t_2^{(A)}$ can be made arbitrarily small, either by increasing the accelerations or by taking a longer trip. That is, we can assume that the acceleration times are negligible compared to the time for the whole trip, and therefore $\Delta T^{(A)} \cong 2\Delta t_2^{(A)}$.

What will B's clock read when he returns? During the coasting periods B's clock will run slow as seen by A, so by the usual time-dilation formula,

$$\Delta t_2^{(B)} = \Delta t_2^{(A)} \sqrt{1 - v^2/c^2}. \tag{E-3}$$

During an accelerating period, B's clock will record a time interval

$$\Delta t_1^{(B)} = \int_0^{\Delta t_1^{(A)}} dt \sqrt{1 - v^2/c^2}. \tag{E-4}$$

Clearly, $\Delta t_1^{(B)} < \Delta t_1^{(A)}$ since the integrand is less than unity over the entire interval. That is, B's clock will run slow while accelerating, but by a varying rate. Since we have already assumed that $\Delta t_1^{(A)}$ is negligible compared to $\Delta t_2^{(A)}$, it follows that $\Delta t_1^{(B)} \ll \Delta t_2^{(A)}$ also. If in addition the coasting velocity is not so high that $\Delta t_2^{(B)}$ is also negligible compared to $\Delta t_2^{(A)}$, we can say that $\Delta t_1^{(B)} \ll \Delta t_2^{(B)}$, and so neglect the periods of acceleration for B's clock also. The final result, therefore, is that from A's point of view, B's clock reads less than A's when they reunite. In fact,

$$\Delta T^{(A)} = \frac{\Delta T^{(B)}}{\sqrt{1 - v^2/c^2}}$$

$$= \Delta T^{(B)} \left(1 + \frac{v^2}{2c^2} + \ldots\right) \tag{E-5}$$

to first order in v^2/c^2, using the binomial expansion.

<u>To B</u>:

The more difficult job remains of discovering why B returns younger than A as seen by B <u>himself</u>! During the coasting periods, while B is at rest in an inertial frame, he is allowed to use special relativity. So during this time, he must find that A's clock runs slow, which would seem to imply that A will be younger than B when the trip is over. Therefore the periods of acceleration must be <u>crucial</u> from B's standpoint, because A must age so fast during these periods that he not only overcomes his slower aging during coasting, but actually ages enough extra to make him older than B at the end, by the factor already found. This miracle is wrought by the gravitational influence on clock-rates derived in Appendix D. The magnitude of the effect is so large during the time that B turns around at Sirius, that this period of acceleration is <u>not</u> negligible from B's point of view.

While B is coasting, time dilation of A's clock gives

$$\Delta t_2^{(A)} = \Delta t_2^{(B)} \sqrt{1 - v^2/c^2} = \Delta t_2^{(B)} (1 - v^2/2c^2 + \ldots) \tag{E-6}$$

to first order in v^2/c^2. While B is accelerating, he feels an effective gravitational field in his frame, which will cause clocks A and B to run at different rates. The clock at "higher altitude" will run faster than the clock at "lower altitude" by the factor $(1+g\ell/c^2)$, where g is the acceleration and ℓ is the distance between them (as measured by B). During the initial and final periods of acceleration, A is at "lower altitudes" than B, so will run slower. The factor $(1+g\ell/c^2)$ will vary continuously, since ℓ changes. But for not too high velocities, $v = \sqrt{2g\ell}$ for uniform acceleration, so $g\ell/c^2 \cong v^2/2c^2$, and $(1+g\ell/c^2)$ will vary from unity to something less than three halves. The

169

acceleration time for B is assumed to be negligible compared to the coasting time, so the same is true for A's clock, since it will read somewhat less than B's clock at the end of the acceleration period.

The situation is quite different, however, when B turns around at the midpoint of his journey. Now it is $\underline{A}$ who is at a "higher altitude, " in fact higher by the distance between the earth and Sirius. In terms of B's total travel time and the velocity while coasting, this distance is $\ell = \dfrac{\Delta T^{(B)}}{2} v$. The acceleration g is the change in velocity divided by the time interval for the acceleration as measured by B, or $2v/\Delta t^{(B)}$. The change in velocity is 2v, because the velocity is first one way and then the other way after the turn-around is completed. Altogether, A runs faster than B by the factor

$$(1 + \frac{g\ell}{c^2}) = 1 + \frac{2v}{\Delta t^{(B)}} \frac{\Delta T^{(B)} v}{2c^2} = 1 + \frac{v^2}{c^2} \frac{\Delta T^{(B)}}{\Delta t^{(B)}} . \qquad \text{(E-7)}$$

So A will advance an amount

$$\Delta t^{(A)} = \Delta t^{(B)} (1 + \frac{v^2}{c^2} \frac{\Delta T^{(B)}}{\Delta t^{(B)}})$$

$$\qquad \text{(E-8)}$$

$$= \Delta t^{(B)} + \frac{v^2}{c^2} \Delta T^{(B)} .$$

The amazing thing about this result is that no matter how fast B turns around ($\Delta t^{(B)} \to 0$), he will see A age by at least $(v^2/c^2)\Delta T^{(B)}$, which is proportional to the time for the entire trip! A is at such high altitudes in B's effective gravitational field that he ages a great deal almost instantaneously from B's point of view. If B were watching through a telescope, A's hair might turn white in a few seconds!

The total time for the trip to B is $\Delta T^{(B)}$, and the total time for A can be found by adding his aging during the turn-around phase to that from the constant-velocity phase. As before, we take $\Delta t^{(B)} \to 0$ relative to

$\Delta t_2^{(B)}$, so $\Delta T^{(A)} = \Delta T^{(B)} (1 - v^2/2c^2 + \ldots)$ (constant velocity part)

$$+ \frac{v^2}{c^2} \Delta T^{(B)} \qquad\qquad \text{(accelerating part)}$$

$$= \Delta T^{(B)} (1 + \frac{v^2}{2c^2} + \ldots) \qquad\qquad \text{(E-9)}$$

which shows that A is older than B at the end of the trip by the same amount (at least to this order in v^2/c^2) as we found before from A's point of view! The new element we've introduced is the gravitational effect on clocks, which must be included when using accelerated frames of reference.

The purpose of the foregoing was to demonstrate the way in which the twin "paradox" can be resolved from the traveling twin's point of view. A number of implicit as well as explicit assumptions have been made. As stated before, a thorough investigation of accelerating frames of reference is both necessary and worthwhile, and leads into the fascinating subject of general relativity.

The twin "paradox" is really no paradox at all. The idea that a contradiction is involved arose from a misunderstanding of the special theory of relativity — namely, that the time-dilation formula could be used in all situations. Since it was derived for inertial frames, it is not at all surprising that it doesn't work for the accelerating twin. The spaceman who goes off to Sirius as in our example really will be younger than his twin brother when he returns.

APPENDIX F

THE "PARADOX" OF LIGHT-SPHERES

AT THE END OF CHAPTER III, an apparently paradoxical conclusion
was drawn from the fact that light moves at the same speed in all inertial frames. If a bomb explodes at the origins of two frames just as
they pass, the resulting light rushes out in a spherical wave-front in
each frame, and furthermore a set of observers in each frame find that
the sphere center is at the origin of their own frame. This seems impossible, since after the origins pass, they no longer coincide.

This result seems paradoxical because everyone is used to implicitly
assuming that simultaneity is an absolute rather than a relative concept. Using the results of Chapter VI on the readings of moving clocks,
we can resolve this paradox, showing why observers in one frame both
measure the sphere center to be at their own origin and also understand
why observers in the other frame measure the center to be at their
origin.

How can observers in a frame set up an experiment capable of discern-
ing the spherical nature of a wave-front? One way would be to station
a number of clocks at equal distances from the origin, synchronize
them, and then measure the time read by each clock as the light passes
by. If they all read the same time, the observers can conclude the light
disperses as a sphere centered about their origin. *

We will suppose that observers in both frames choose to use this method,
and that in particular they station their clocks at a distance of 30 light-
minutes from their own origin. Besides measuring this distance, observers in each frame properly synchronize their clocks, according to
the prescription of Chapter VI. We'll view events from the unprimed
frame, verifying that the wave spreads out symmetrically from our
origin, and also will see why primed observers think the wave is centered at their origin.

---

* There is no doubt about the outcome of the experiment, because one
method of synchronizing clocks is identical to the experiment itself.

172

Let the primed frame move to our right at speed $V = \frac{3}{5} c$. Figure F.1 shows the situation as the frame origins coincide and the bomb explodes. Four clocks are shown in each frame, with all unprimed clocks synchronized at $t = 0$. The two primed clocks on the x'-axis are unsynchronized from our point of view: the one on the right reads $t = - vD/c^2$, and the one on the left reads $t = + vD/c^2$, according to the rules of Chapter VI, where D is the rest-distance of each clock from the origin. The distance of each of these clocks from <u>our</u> origin is only $D \sqrt{1 - V^2/c^2} = \frac{4}{5} D$ as we see them, owing to the Lorentz contraction. In our example, $\frac{4}{5} D = \frac{4}{5} \times 30 = 24$ light-minutes, and the deviations from synchronization are

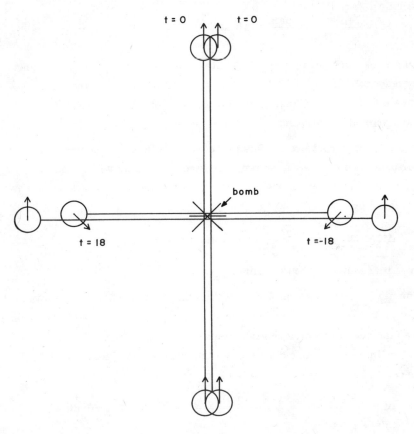

Figure F.1

173

$$\frac{vD}{c^2} = \frac{V}{c} \cdot \frac{D}{c} = \frac{3}{5} \times \frac{30 \text{ light-minutes}}{c} = 18 \text{ minutes}$$

as shown in Figure F.1.

As the light spreads out at the same speed in all directions, the first clock it meets is the left-hand primed clock, since that clock is moving toward the origin of our frame. This clock was originally a distance

$$30 \sqrt{1 - v^2/c^2} = 30 \times \frac{4}{5} = 24 \text{ light-minutes}$$

from our origin. So when this clock meets the light wave, the distance traveled by the clock plus the distance traveled by the light wave must be $v\Delta t + c\Delta t = \frac{3}{5} c\Delta t + c\Delta t = 24$ light-minutes, so

$$\Delta t = \frac{24 \text{ light-minutes}}{\frac{8}{5} c} = 15 \text{ minutes.}$$

Our clocks will advance by 15 minutes, but primed clocks will advance by only $\Delta t' = \Delta t \sqrt{1 - v^2/c^2} = 15 \cdot \frac{4}{5} = 12$ minutes, by the effect of time dilation. The situation is shown in Figure F.2. Note that the left-hand primed clock reads t = 30 minutes.

The next important event takes place when the wave-front intercepts our unprimed clocks, as shown in Figure F.3. This will happen 30 minutes after the experiment starts. Each primed clock will have advanced by only

$$\Delta t' = 30 \sqrt{1 - v^2/c^2} = 30 \times \frac{4}{5} = 24 \text{ minutes}$$

over its reading at the beginning.

The next important event happens when the light reaches the two primed clocks on the y'-axis, as shown in Figure F.4. By the law of Pythagoras the distance of these clocks from our origin is $\sqrt{D^2 + v^2 \Delta t^2}$ where Δt is the time read by our clocks when the event takes place. But this distance is also $c\Delta t$, so $c^2 \Delta t^2 = D^2 + v^2 \Delta t^2$, or

$$\Delta t = \frac{D/c}{\sqrt{1 - v^2/c^2}} = \frac{5}{4} \times \frac{30 \text{ light-minutes}}{c} = 37\text{-}1/2 \text{ minutes.}$$

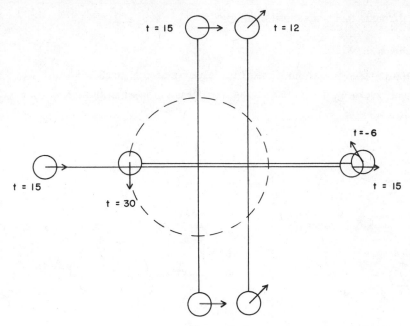

t = 15
t = 12
t = 15
t = -6
t = 15
t = 30

Figure F.2

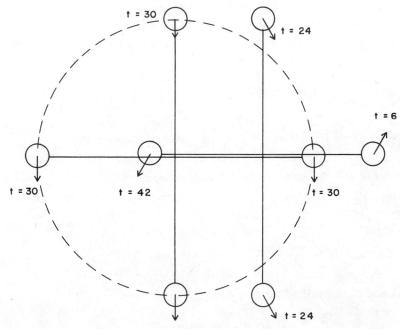

t = 30
t = 24
t = 6
t = 30
t = 42
t = 30
t = 24

Figure F.3

175

The primed clocks advanced by only

$$37\text{-}1/2 \sqrt{1 - V^2/c^2} = 30 \text{ minutes}$$

from their position at the start of the experiment. Note that the two primed clocks on the y' axis read t = 30 minutes when the light hits them.

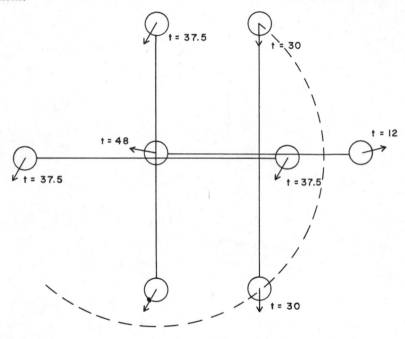

Figure F.4

Finally, light from the explosion will catch up with the right-hand primed clocks, as shown in Figure F.5. The total distance from the origin is 24 light-minutes (the original distance of the clock from our origin) plus vΔt. This distance is also covered by the light wave, so

$$c\Delta t = 24 + v\Delta t = 24 + \frac{3}{5} c\Delta t$$

or $\Delta t = \dfrac{24 \text{ light-minutes}}{\dfrac{2}{5} c} = 60 \text{ minutes.}$

Primed clocks will advance by only

$$60 \sqrt{1 - V^2/c^2} = \frac{4}{5} \, 60 = 48 \text{ minutes}$$

176

past their reading at the beginning of the experiment. The right-hand primed clock reads t = 30 minutes when the light hits it.

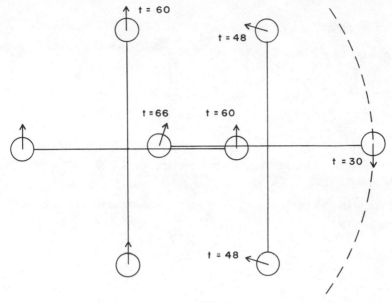

Figure F.5

Notice that even from <u>our</u> point of view, not only any of our unprimed clocks, but also <u>every primed clock</u> receives the light signal when it reads t = 30 minutes. Thus the primed observers have an equal right to claim the light-sphere is centered at their own origin. All their clocks receive the light at the same time from their point of view.

FORCES AND ELECTROMAGNETISM

IN CHAPTER XIV the Lorentz force

$$\vec{F} = q \, (\vec{E} + \vec{v} \times \vec{B}) \tag{14-3}$$

and the relativistic equation of motion

$$\vec{F} = \frac{d\vec{p}}{dt} \tag{14-9}$$

were written down. In this appendix we'll discuss forces and electro-magnetism somewhat further. In particular, we'll find the transformation rules for force, show how Minkowski invented a four-vector force, and then briefly introduce the relationship between relativity and electromagnetism.

1. The Force Transformation

In Newtonian mechanics, a force has a strength which is independent of the observer's inertial reference frame. This is consistent with the equation of motion $\vec{F} = m\vec{a}$, since the mass and acceleration are also the same in all inertial frames. We can find out how <u>relativistic forces</u> change from frame to frame by figuring out how the quantity $\frac{d\vec{p}}{dt}$ transforms, since $\vec{F} = \frac{d\vec{p}}{dt}$, as shown in Chapter XIV. The momentum $\vec{p}$ was shown to be part of a four-vector p_μ in Chapter XIII. But the force $\vec{F}$ cannot be part of a four-vector also, because the time t changes from one frame to another. If t <u>were</u> a scalar (the same to anyone), the force <u>would</u> transform like a four-vector, making our problem easy.

In order to find the correct rules for transforming $\vec{F}$, we require that the relativistic equation of motion be valid in two inertial frames, the "primed" and "unprimed" frames:

$$\vec{F} = \frac{d\vec{p}}{dt} \quad \text{and} \quad \vec{F}' = \frac{d\vec{p}'}{dt'} \; .$$

Taking them one component at a time, in the x-direction

$$F_x = \frac{dp_x}{dt} \text{ and } F_x' = \frac{dp_x'}{dt'} \; .$$

But

$$p_x' = \gamma(p_x - V\,E/c^2) \text{ and } t' = \gamma(t - V\,x/c^2) \text{ (equations 12-5 and 7-6)}$$

so

$$F_x' = \frac{d\{\gamma\,(p_x - V\,E/c^2)\}}{d\{\gamma\,(t - V\,x/c^2)\}} = \frac{\dfrac{dp_x}{dt} - \dfrac{V}{c^2}\dfrac{dE}{dt}}{1 - \dfrac{V}{c^2}\dfrac{dx}{dt}} \quad .$$

Equation (14-18) gives $\dfrac{dE}{dt} = \vec{v} \cdot \vec{F}$,

so finally

$$F_x' = \frac{F_x - V/c^2\,(\vec{v} \cdot \vec{F})}{1 - v_x\,V/c^2} \tag{G-1}$$

is the rule for finding F_x'. The equations for F_y' and F_z' are even easier to find, since $p_y' = p_y$ and $p_z' = p_z$. The results are

$$F_y' = \frac{F_y}{\gamma(1 - \dfrac{v_x V}{c^2})} \tag{G-2}$$

and

$$F_z' = \frac{F_z}{\gamma(1 - \dfrac{v_x V}{c^2})} \quad . \tag{G-3}$$

As usual, the inverse transformation follows by changing the sign of V and interchanging primes and unprimes:

$$F_x = \frac{F_x' + \dfrac{V}{c^2}\vec{v}' \cdot \vec{F}'}{1 + \dfrac{v_x'V}{c^2}} \tag{G-4}$$

$$F_y = \frac{F_y'}{\gamma(1 + \frac{v_x'V}{c^2})}$$

(G-4 Cont)

$$F_z = \frac{F_z'}{\gamma(1 + \frac{v_x'V}{c^2})} \; .$$

In the non-relativistic limit, where all velocities are much smaller than c, the rules reduce to $\vec{F}' = \vec{F}$ as expected.

A particularly useful transformation of relativistic forces is that between the rest-frame of a particle and some other frame. Suppose a particle is instantaneously at rest in the primed frame, where it feels a force with components F_x', F_y', and F_z'. Since $\vec{v}' = 0$, the transformation gives:

$$F_x = F_x'$$

$$F_y = \frac{F_y'}{\gamma} = F_y'\sqrt{1 - V^2/c^2} \text{ and} \qquad (G-5)$$

$$F_z = \frac{F_z'}{\gamma} = F_z'\sqrt{1 - V^2/c^2} \; .$$

So, except in the x-direction, the force in the proper frame, which is the particle's instantaneous rest frame, is greater than the force in any other frame. We'll use these equations in Section 3 to find the rules for transforming the electric and magnetic fields.

2. The Minkowski Force

As just shown, the force $\vec{F}$ transforms in a rather complicated way, and is not part of a four-vector. The most easily seen "cause" of this situation is that taking the time derivative $\frac{dp_\mu}{dt}$ spoils the four-vector p_μ, since time depends on the frame of reference. It was Minkowski who first showed that it is possible to define a four-vector force by differentiating a particle's momentum by its proper time. As pointed out before, the proper time τ, which is the time read by a clock carried along with the particle, is a scalar quantity, the same in all frames.

Since τ doesn't depend upon the reference frame, $\dfrac{dp_\mu}{d\tau}$ transforms like p_μ itself, and is therefore a four-vector. Minkowski's idea then was to <u>define</u> a four-vector K_μ by

$$K_\mu = \frac{dp_\mu}{d\tau}, \qquad\qquad (G-6)$$

known today as the Minkowski force.

Since an infinitesimal proper time $d\tau$ is related to an infinitesimal time dt in an observer's frame by the time-dilation factor, we have

$$K_\mu = \frac{dp_\mu}{d\tau} = \frac{dp_\mu}{\sqrt{1 - v^2/c^2}\, dt} = \frac{F_\mu}{\sqrt{1 - v^2/c^2}} = \gamma F_\mu \ (\mu = 1,\ 2,\ 3) \qquad (G-7)$$

where the quantities F_μ are the components of the ordinary force-vector $\vec{F}$. The fourth component of K_μ is

$$K_4 = \frac{dp_4}{d\tau} = \frac{1}{\sqrt{1 - v^2/c^2}} \frac{d}{dt}\, i\, E/c = \frac{i\gamma}{c} \frac{dE}{dt}\ . \qquad (G-8)$$

Equation (14-18) gives $\dfrac{dE}{dt} = \vec{F} \cdot \vec{v}$, so the Minkowski force components can be written

$$K_\mu = (\gamma F_x,\ \gamma F_y,\ \gamma F_z,\ \frac{i\gamma}{c} \vec{F} \cdot \vec{v})\ . \qquad (G-9)$$

Because K_μ is a four-vector, it transforms just like the position or momentum four-vectors.

From the definition of K_μ, and from its relationship with the ordinary force, it is easy to see that the equations of motion

$$\vec{F} = \frac{d\vec{p}}{dt} \text{ and } K_\mu = \frac{dp_\mu}{d\tau}\ (\mu = 1,\ 2,\ 3)$$

are completely equivalent, while the $\mu = 4$ equation merely defines K_4, so tells nothing new. Therefore the introduction of the Minkowski force mostly serves to show that the relativistic equation of motion <u>can</u> be written in the elegant four-dimensional form. Since the relationship with electric and magnetic fields is more direct with the ordinary force $\vec{F}$, the equation $\vec{F} = \dfrac{d\vec{p}}{dt}$ is most often used in practice.

3. The Electric and Magnetic Field Transformations

As pointed out at the beginning of Chapter XIV, it is reasonable to expect that electric and magnetic fields depend upon the observer's frame of reference. We are now equipped to find these transformation laws, by making use of the Lorentz force equation $\vec{F} = q(\vec{E} + \vec{v} \times \vec{B})$ and the rules for transforming forces derived in Section 1. A rigorous development of the field transformations is best achieved by introducing the electromagnetic field tensor, a program which is carried out by several of the references listed at the end of this appendix. However, the following more awkward derivation follows from what we've done already.

Suppose a charge q is instantaneously at <u>rest</u> in the <u>primed</u> frame. If there is an electric field $\vec{E}'$ and magnetic field $\vec{B}'$ in this frame, the charge will feel an electric force $q\vec{E}'$, but no magnetic force. Now we would like to relate this force in the primed frame to the force acting on the particle in the <u>unprimed</u> frame. This is accomplished by the force transformation equations (G-5)

$$F_x' = F_x$$
$$F_y' = \gamma F_y \qquad\qquad (G-5)$$
$$F_z' = \gamma F_z$$

for particles at rest in the primed frame. In terms of fields, the Lorentz force equation

$$\vec{F} = q\,(\vec{E} + \vec{v} \times \vec{B})$$

can be used in the F_x' equation to give

$$qE_x' = q \left\{ E_x + (\vec{v} \times \vec{B})_x \right\} = q\,E_x$$

because $(\vec{v} \times \vec{B})_x = 0$, since the charge moves in the x-direction in the unprimed frame. The transformation for E_x' is therefore simply

182

$E_x' = E_x$. The F_y' equation requires that $E_y' = \gamma \{ E_y + (\vec{v} \times \vec{B})_y \}$ and the F_z' equation gives $E_z' = \gamma \{ E_z + (\vec{v} \times \vec{B})_z \}$.

Altogether, the electric field transformation can be summarized in the equations

$$E_{||}' = E_{||} \quad \text{and}$$
$$\vec{E}_\perp' = \gamma \{ \vec{E}_\perp + (\vec{V} \times \vec{B})_\perp \} \tag{G-10}$$

saying that the component of $\vec{E}$ parallel to the relative velocity of the two frames is unchanged, while the two perpendicular components mix $\vec{E}$ and $\vec{B}$.

The transformation rules for the magnetic field $\vec{B}$ are harder to derive, since magnetic forces are velocity dependent. They are derived here by using a particular situation, but the results are general, which can be checked by trying other situations. Let a particle move in the y' direction in the primed frame, so that $\vec{F}' = q (\vec{E}' + \vec{v} \times \vec{B}')$ has components $F_x' = q (E_x' + v'B_z')$; $F_y' = q E_y'$; $F_z' = q (E_z' - v'B_x')$.

In the unprimed frame, the particle moves in the x-direction as well, with components

$$v_x = V, \quad v_y = \frac{v_y'}{\gamma(1 + V\frac{x}{c^2})} = \frac{v_y'}{\gamma} = \frac{v'}{\gamma}, \quad \text{and } v_z = 0,$$

as shown in Figure G.1. These equations were derived directly from the velocity transformation (7-11).

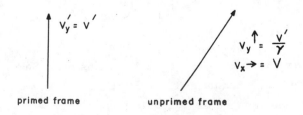

primed frame   unprimed frame

Figure G.1

The components of $\vec{F} = q\{\vec{E} + (\vec{v} \times \vec{B})\}$ are $F_x = q(E_x + v_y B_z)$, $F_y = q(E_y - VB_z)$, and $F_z = q(E_z + VB_y - v_y B_x)$.

Having obtained the force components in each frame, they can be related by the inverse force transformation equations (G-4):

$$F_x = \frac{F_x' + \dfrac{V}{c^2}\vec{F}' \cdot \vec{v}'}{1 + \dfrac{Vv_x'}{c^2}} = F_x' + \frac{V}{c^2}v_y'F_y'$$

$$F_y = \frac{F_y'}{\gamma(1 + \dfrac{Vv_x'}{c^2})} = \frac{F_y'}{\gamma} \quad \text{and} \qquad \text{(G-11)}$$

$$F_z = \frac{F_z'}{\gamma}.$$

In terms of fields, the F_x equation becomes

$$E_x + v_y B_z = E_x' + v'B_z' + \frac{V v'}{c^2}E_y'$$

$$\text{or} \quad v'B_z' = v_y B_z + E_x - E_x' - \frac{V v'}{c^2}E_y'. \qquad \text{(G-12)}$$

The electric field transformations

$$E_x' = E_x \quad \text{and} \quad E_y' = \gamma(E_y - v_x B_z)$$

can be used in (G-12) to give

$$B_z' = \frac{v_y}{v'}B_z - \frac{V}{c^2}\gamma(E_y - vB_z)$$

$$= (\frac{1}{\gamma} + \frac{\gamma V^2}{c^2})B_z - \frac{\gamma V}{c^2}E_y \qquad \text{(G-13)}$$

$$\text{or} \quad B_z' = \gamma(B_z - (V \times E)_z/c^2).$$

The F_y transformation is $E_y - VB_z = \frac{1}{\gamma}E_y'$ in terms of the fields, but the electric field transformation gives $\gamma E_y' = E_y - VB_z$, so the F_y transformation reduces to an identity, telling us nothing new.

184

From the F_z equation,

$$E_z + V B_y - v_y B_x = \frac{1}{\gamma} (E_z' - v'B_x'),$$

or $v'B_x' = -\gamma (E_z + V B_y) + E_z' + \gamma v_y B_x$ (G-14)

$$= \gamma v_y B_x$$

using the transformation for E_z'. Therefore, since $v_y = \frac{1}{\gamma} v'$, this reduces to

$$B_x' = B_x ,$$ (G-15)

another of the transformations.

The rule for transforming B_y' can be derived by letting the particle move in the z direction instead of in the y direction. By symmetry with the z direction, it is clear that

$$B_y' = \gamma (B_y - (\vec{V} \times \vec{E})_y/c^2)$$ (G-16)

so that altogether

$$B_{||}' = B_{||} \quad \text{and}$$

$$\vec{B}_\perp' = \gamma (\vec{B}_\perp - (\vec{V} \times \vec{E})_\perp /c^2)$$ (G-17)

which appear very similar to the $\vec{E}$ transformations, differing only in the minus sign and in the position of the c^2 factor.

4.   Applications of the Field Transformations

The transformations for $\vec{E}$ and $\vec{B}$ lead immediately to some interesting consequences. The first of these is the phenomenon of electromagnetic induction. Suppose a U-shaped piece of wire is placed in a uniform field B, and a sliding wire is placed on it so as to complete the circuit, as shown in Figure G.2.

185

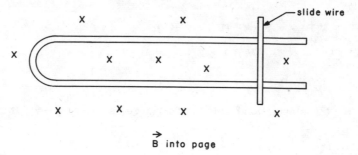

$\vec{B}$ into page

Figure G.2

No current flows in the circuit, because there is no electric field which could cause electrons in the wires to move about. But suppose that the sliding wire is pulled to the right with steady speed v, without breaking contact with the U-shaped wire. Then in the frame of the slide-wire, which we'll call the primed frame, the electric field transformation (G-10) gives

$$E_{||}' = E_{||} = 0, \text{ but}$$

$$\vec{E}_\perp' = \gamma(\vec{E}_\perp + (\vec{v} \times \vec{B})_\perp) = \gamma(\vec{v} \times \vec{B})_\perp \qquad \text{(G-18)}$$

which corresponds to an electric field pointing vertically upward along the slide wire. This causes current to flow in the circuit, as shown in Figure G.3.

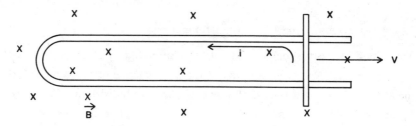

Figure G.3

We've built a simple electric generator. In most laboratory situations the velocity is small, so the factor γ can be neglected, leaving $\vec{E}' = \vec{v} \times \vec{B}$. The induced electromotive force, defined as the line integral of the electric field around the circuit, is

186

$$\mathcal{E} = \int \vec{E} \cdot d\vec{\ell} + \int \vec{E} \cdot d\vec{\ell} = 0 + vB\ell$$
$$\quad\ \ \text{U-shaped} \quad \text{slide}$$
$$\quad\ \ \ \ \ \text{wire} \quad\quad \text{wire}$$

or

$$\mathcal{E} = B\ell v, \qquad\qquad\qquad\qquad (G\text{-}19)$$

where ℓ is the length of the slide wire between the sides of the U.

The field transformation can also be used to find the electric and magnetic fields outside a uniformly moving electric charge. If a charge q is at rest at the origin of the primed frame, Coulomb's law says that the electric field in that frame is

$$\vec{E'} = \frac{q \, \hat{r}'}{4\pi\epsilon_o \, r'^2} \qquad\qquad\qquad\qquad (G\text{-}20)$$

in MKS units, where $\hat{r}'$ is a unit vector in the radial direction, and ϵ_o is the permittivity of the vacuum.* In component form

$$E_x' = \frac{qx'}{4\pi\epsilon_o r'^3} \, ; \ \ E_y' = \frac{qy'}{4\pi\epsilon_o r'^3} \, ; \ \text{and} \ E_z' = \frac{qz'}{4\pi\epsilon_o r'^3} \, .$$

If this charge is viewed from the unprimed frame, it will be moving to the right at speed V. We can transform to unprimed coordinates by recalling that a distance x' in the primed frame appears to be a distance $x = \frac{x'}{\gamma}$ in the unprimed frame, but that y' = y, and z' = z. Therefore

$$r'^2 = x'^2 + y'^2 + z'^2 = \gamma^2 x^2 + y^2 + z^2 \, . \qquad\qquad (G\text{-}21)$$

Measuring an angle θ from the x-axis, as shown in Figure G.4, we can write $x = r \cos\theta$ and $y^2 + z^2 = r^2 \sin^2\theta$.

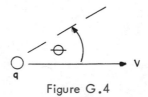

Figure G.4

---

* ϵ_o is a constant $\cong 8.85 \times 10^{12}$.

187

so

$$r'^2 = \gamma^2 r^2 \left[\cos^2\theta + \frac{1}{\gamma^2}\sin^2\theta\right] = \gamma^2 r^2 \left(1 - \frac{V^2}{c^2}\sin^2\theta\right). \qquad \text{(G-22)}$$

The field transformations (G-10) for $\vec{E}$ give $E_x = E_x'$, $E_y = \gamma E_y'$ and $E_z = \gamma E_z'$ (since $\vec{B'} = 0$) from which we get altogether

$$\vec{E} = \frac{q\,\hat{r}}{4\pi\epsilon_0\gamma^2 r^2 (1 - V^2/c^2 \sin^2\theta)^{3/2}} \qquad \text{(G-23)}$$

showing that the electric field of a moving charge is still radial in direction, but is no longer spherically symmetric. The field lines are squashed up, as shown in Figure G.5.

The electric field is small along the direction of motion, but is large in the perpendicular directions. Note that the distortion is of order V^2/c^2, so the charge must be relativistic before the departure from spherical symmetry is appreciable.

The magnetic field transformation (G-17) gives

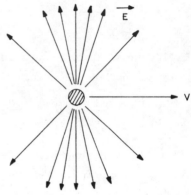

Figure G.5

$$B_x = B_x' = 0$$

$$\vec{B}_\perp = \gamma\left(\vec{B'}_\perp + (\vec{V}\times\vec{E'})_\perp/c^2\right) = \frac{\gamma}{c^2}(\vec{V}\times\vec{E'}) . \qquad \text{(G-24)}$$

or

$$\vec{B} = \frac{q\,\vec{V}\times\hat{r}}{4\pi\epsilon_0 c^2\gamma^2 r^2 (1 - \frac{V^2}{c^2}\sin^2\theta)^{3/2}}.$$

The permeability of the vacuum μ_0 is related to the permittivity ϵ_0 and the speed of light by

$$\mu_0 = \frac{1}{\epsilon_0 c^2} , \qquad \text{(G-25)}$$

so

$$\vec{B} = \frac{\mu_0 \, q \, \vec{V} \times \hat{r}}{4\pi\gamma^2 r^2 \, (1 - \frac{V^2}{c^2} \sin^2\theta)^{3/2}} \qquad \text{(G-26)}$$

In the limit of low velocities,

$$\vec{B} = \frac{\mu_0 \, q \, \vec{V} \times \hat{r}}{4\pi \, r^2} \qquad \text{(G-27)}$$

which is known as the law of Biot and Savart.

5. Fields and Forces Outside a Wire

To gain insight into why the electric and magnetic fields transform as
they do, it is helpful to understand how the fields arise from their
sources, which are electric charges and currents. Since a stationary
distribution of charge in one frame will appear as a current in another
frame, we might expect to be able to calculate the corresponding
changes in the fields.

The exact mathematical connection between the fields and their sources
is contained in Maxwell's equations of electromagnetism. The equations
are easy to solve if the charges and currents are simple and symmetrical,
but in general only numerical solutions are possible. We'll treat here the
special case of an infinite wire bearing a net uniform charge per unit
length, and carrying in addition a steady current i. In MKS units, the
fields outside the wire are

$$E = \frac{\lambda}{2\pi\epsilon_0 r} \quad \text{and} \quad B = \frac{\mu_0 i}{2\pi r} \qquad \text{(G-28)}$$

where r is the distance from the wire, λ is expressed in Coulombs/
meter, and i in Coulombs/second, or amperes. The electric field
vectors point directly away from or toward the wire, depending on whether
λ is positive or negative. The magnetic field vectors point in circular
paths around the wire, as shown in Figure G.6.

189

The current inside a wire is related in a simple way to the charge
density and the velocity of moving
charges. Usually it is the negative electrons in a wire which
carry the current. If the charge
density of moving electrons is λ_-
and their average velocity is v_-,

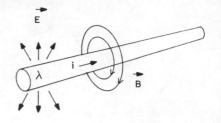

Figure G.6

the current (being the charge/sec passing a given place in the wire) is
$i = \lambda_- v_-$. The <u>conventional</u> current is in the opposite direction to the motion of the electrons. Positive ions at rest in the wire contribute a charge
density λ_+, which is usually equal to λ_-, so that there is no net charge
density.

From the Lorentz force equation, a charge q <u>outside</u> the wire will experience an electric force

$$F_E = q \, E = \frac{q \, \lambda}{2\pi \epsilon_o r} \qquad\qquad \text{(G-29)}$$

and if it is moving with velocity $\vec{v}$, it will also feel a magnetic force
$q \, (\vec{v} \times \vec{B})$. In the special case of motion parallel to the wire, the magnetic
force is

$$F_B = \frac{q\mu_o i}{2\pi r} \, v \qquad\qquad \text{(G-30)}$$

either away from or toward the wire, depending upon the velocity direction and the sign of the charge.

From these equations, we can calculate the force on charged particles
outside the wire, as viewed from various frames of reference. For
example, suppose the charge is at rest outside a stationary wire carrying a current, as shown in Figure G.7.

190

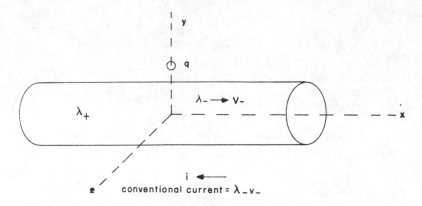

We suppose that $\lambda_+ = \lambda_-$, so there is no net charge on the wire in this frame of reference, and there is therefore no electric force on q. There isn't any magnetic force either, because the charged particle isn't moving. It remains at rest, without accelerating.

Now consider the situation in a primed frame moving to the right at speed $V = v_-$, a convenient choice since now the negative charge is at rest, while the positive charge moves to the left at speed V. By calculating the charges and currents in this frame, the force $\vec{F}'$ on q can be found. With no work at all, we know this force must be zero because if a charge doesn't accelerate in one inertial frame, it can't accelerate in any other inertial frame. (The fact that $\vec{F}' = 0$ is also a trivial consequence of the force transformation laws.)

It is instructive to verify this expectation by calculating the charges, currents, and forces. Since the positive particles are moving in the primed frame, they are closer together than in the original frame by the Lorentz contraction effect, increasing the charge density to

$$\lambda_+' = \lambda_+ \Big/ \sqrt{1 - V^2/c^2} \ . \tag{G-31}$$

But now the negative particles aren't moving, so are farther apart than before, decreasing the density to

$$\lambda_-' = \lambda_- \sqrt{1 - V^2/c^2} \ . \tag{G-32}$$

191

The net charge density on the wire is therefore

$$\lambda' = \lambda_+' - \lambda_-' = \lambda_+ \left(\frac{1}{\sqrt{1 - V^2/c^2}} - \sqrt{1 - V^2/c^2} \right)$$

$$= \frac{\lambda_+}{\sqrt{1 - V^2/c^2}} \frac{V^2}{c^2} \tag{G-33}$$

since $\lambda_+ = \lambda_-$. This corresponds to a net positive charge, which will repel the charge q by an electric force

$$F_E' = \frac{q\lambda'}{2\pi\epsilon_o r} = \frac{q\lambda_+}{2\pi\epsilon_o r \sqrt{1 - V^2/c^2}} \frac{V^2}{c^2} . \tag{G-34}$$

But now the charge q is moving to the left at speed V, so will also experience a magnetic force

$$F_B' = \frac{q\mu_o i'}{2\pi r} V = \frac{q\mu_o \lambda_+' V^2}{2\pi r} = \frac{q\mu_o \lambda_+ V^2}{2\pi r \sqrt{1 - V^2/c^2}} \tag{G-35}$$

toward the wire (the direction can be verified by looking at $\vec{F}' = q\,(\vec{V}' \times \vec{B}')$.)
We have used $i' = \lambda_+' V$, and $\lambda_+' = \lambda_+ / \sqrt{1 - V^2/c^2}$. Using finally $\mu_o = \frac{1}{\epsilon_o c^2}$, it is seen that the magnetic and electric forces are equal and opposite, producing no net force, as expected.

There is another way to verify that the force on the charge is zero in the primed frame. Instead of recalculating the charge density and current and the forces they produce, we can transform the electric and magnetic fields, and then the force by the Lorentz equation $\vec{F} = q\,(\vec{E} + \vec{v} \times \vec{B})$. This is a good example of using the $\vec{E}$ and $\vec{B}$ transformations.

In the original (unprimed) frame, the electric field $\vec{E}$ due to the wire is zero, because the wire has no net charge. The magnetic field around the wire is

$$B = \frac{\mu_o i}{2\pi r} = \frac{\mu_o}{2\pi r} \lambda_- V_- ,$$ circulating as shown in Figure G.8.

192

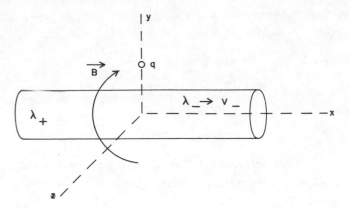

Figure G.8

At the position of the charge

$$B_x = B_y = 0 \quad \text{and} \quad B_z = -\frac{\mu_0}{2\pi r}\lambda_- v_-$$

(the minus sign refers to the fact that $\vec{B}$ points in the negative z-direction).

The charge experiences no force, because both E and v_- are zero.

In the primed frame, traveling to the right at speed $V = v_-$, the transformation for $\vec{E}'$ gives

$$E_x' = E_x = 0$$

$$E_y' = \gamma \left\{ E_y + (\vec{V} \times \vec{B})_y \right\}$$

$$= 0 + \gamma (- V B_z) = -\gamma V B_z \qquad \text{(G-36)}$$

$$= \gamma V \frac{\mu_0}{2\pi r}\lambda_- V_-$$

since V is in the x-direction, and $\vec{B}$ is in the minus z-direction. Also $E_z' = \gamma \left\{ E_z + (\vec{V} \times \vec{B})_z \right\} = 0 + 0 = 0$. Thus in the primed frame, the particle feels an electric field pointing away from the wire.

The transformation for $\vec{B}'$ gives

$$B_x' = B_x = 0$$

$$B_y' = \gamma \left\{ B_y - (\vec{V} \times \vec{E})_y / c^2 \right\} = 0 + 0 = 0 \quad \text{and} \qquad \text{(G-37)}$$

$$B_z' = \gamma \left\{ B_z - (\vec{V} \times \vec{E})_z / c^2 \right\} = \gamma B_z \ .$$

193

The magnetic field still points in the same direction, but is γ times larger than in the unprimed frame.

The electric force on the charge is

$$\vec{F}_E{}' = q\ \vec{E}' = q\frac{\mu_o}{2\pi r}\ \lambda_-\ V^2 \text{ away from the wire. The magnetic force is}$$

$$\vec{F}_B{}' = q\ (\vec{v}' \times \vec{B}') + q\ (-v_x B_z{}') = -\ q\ V\frac{\mu_o}{2\pi r}\ \lambda_-\ V$$

since the particle's velocity is in the negative x-direction, and $B_z{}'$ is along the negative z-direction. The total force is therefore again zero, due to cancellation.

REFERENCES

Relativistic electromagnetism is written in four-dimensional form in such books as

1. The Feynman Lectures on Physics, Volume II, by Feynman, Leighton, and Sands (Addison-Wesley, 1964);

2. Classical Electrodynamics by J. D. Jackson (John Wiley and Sons, 1962);

3. The Classical Theory of Fields, by Landau and Lifshitz (Addison-Wesley, 1962);

4. Classical Electricity and Magnetism by Panofsky and Phillips (Addison-Wesley, 1955).

APPENDIX H
THE INTERFERENCE OF LIGHT WAVES

THE MICHELSON-MORLEY EXPERIMENT discussed in Chapter II
was an important link in the chain of evidence discrediting the ether
theory. That experiment was based on the very sensitive measurements possible with the interference of light waves. This appendix
is intended as a brief introduction to the subject for those readers
who haven't previously run across it.

An ideal sinusoidal wave is pictured in Figure H.1. This could be a
graph of the height of water in a water wave, of the density of air in

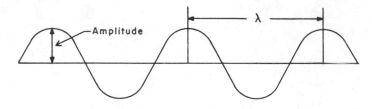

Figure H.1

a sound wave, or of the magnitude of the electric field in a light wave,
all as a function of position at a given time. (Alternatively, it could be
a plot of any of these quantities as a function of <u>time</u> at a given <u>position</u>.)
The maximum height of the wave is called the amplitude, and the dis-
tance between successive maxima is called the wavelength on a position
plot, or the period T on a time plot.

Now what happens if two such waves are combined?   It is predicted
theoretically, and verified experimentally, that if the wave amplitudes
are not too large, the two waves should simply be added point by point.
We'll specialize here to the case where they have the same amplitude
and wavelength, which is appropriate for application to the Michelson
interferometer. If the waves are "in phase," with maxima at the same
place, the sum is a similar wave of twice the amplitude, as shown
in Figure H.2. This situation is called <u>constructive</u> interference, and
produces a bright fringe in the interferometer. If the waves are

195

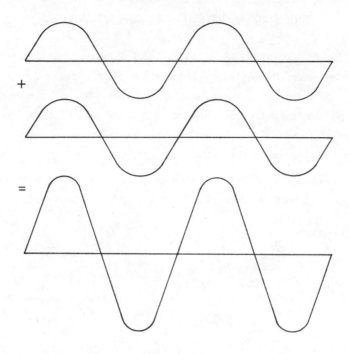

+
=

Figure H.2

completely "out of phase," they sum to zero everywhere, giving <u>de-</u>
<u>structive</u> interference, as shown in Figure H.3. Any other combination
of the waves produces a total wave with amplitude somewhere between
these two extremes, such as the case pictured in Figure H.4.

As described in Chapter II, the Michelson interferometer separates
the original light-beam into two beams which follow different paths and
then recombine. If the paths have different lengths, or if the light
moves at different velocities in different directions (as was thought to
happen in the ether theory), it is unlikely that the waves will be in phase
when they recombine. A time difference of half a period between the
two paths can change constructive into destructive interference. For
6000 Angstrom light, this corresponds to a path difference of only 3000
Angstroms = 3×10^{-5} centimeters, illustrating the high sensitivity of
the interferometer. On the basis of the ether theory, the up- and

196

downstream time is longer than the cross-current time for equal path lengths, producing interference when the beams recombine. When the interferometer is rotated 90°, exchanging the two paths, the interference pattern should change. The extent of the change is a measure of the ether velocity. It was the absence of an experimental fringe shift which helped to undermine the ether theory.

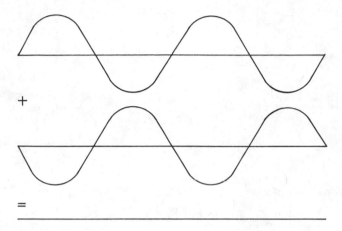

Figure H.3

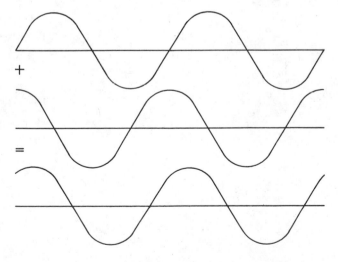

Figure H.4

APPENDIX I
SOME PARTICLES

Family	Particle	Mass-Energy (Mev)	Mean Lifetime (seconds)
Photon	γ	0	∞
Leptons	ν	0	∞
	$e^{\pm}$	0.511	∞
	$\mu^{\pm}$	105.6	2.2×10^{-6}
Mesons	π^{0}	135.0	$\sim 2 \times 10^{-16}$
	$\pi^{\pm}$	139.6	2.5×10^{-8}
	$K^{\pm}$	493.9	1.2×10^{-8}
	K^{0}	497.8	$K_1^{0}: 1.0 \times 10^{-10}$
			$K_2^{0}: 6 \times 10^{-8}$
	η	548	$\sim 10^{-23}$
Baryons	p	936.5	∞
	n	938.2	10^{3}
	Λ^{0}	1115	2.5×10^{-10}
	Σ^{+}	1189	0.8×10^{-10}
	Σ^{0}	1191	$< 0.1 \times 10^{-10}$
	Σ^{-}	1196	1.6×10^{-10}
	Ξ^{0}	1311	$\sim 1.5 \times 10^{-10}$
	Ξ^{-}	1318	$\sim 1.3 \times 10^{-10}$
Vector Mesons	$\rho^{\pm}, \rho^{0}$	750	$\sim 10^{-23}$
	ω^{0}	782	$\sim 10^{-23}$
	$K^{*\pm}, K^{*0}$	888	$\sim 10^{-23}$
	ϕ^{0}	1020	$\sim 10^{-23}$

ANSWERS TO PROBLEMS

CHAPTER I

1. $x'(t') = (v_0 - V) t' + \frac{1}{2} a t'^2$

   $v'(t') = (v_0 - V) + at'$

2. 10 miles/hour   no.

3. $v_x^B = 6$ m/sec, $v_y^A = 8$ m/sec, $v_y^B = -8$ m/sec.

CHAPTER II

1. 2.6×10^{-5} radians

2. 400 seconds, $200\sqrt{3}$ seconds

CHAPTER III

1. a. yes   b. no

CHAPTER IV

1. 3/4 light-hours

2. $v = .8c$

3. $v = (1 - 3.125 \times 10^{-10}) c$

4. a. 4.167×10^{-8} sec.
   b. 4.167×10^{-8} sec.

CHAPTER V

1. a. 1.01×10^5 years
   b. 1.43×10^4 years
   c. 1.414×10^4 light-years

2. a. $v = c\sqrt{2}$
   b. $100/\sqrt{2}$ meters

3. 3.1 inches, 2.6×10^{-10} sec., 1.075×10^{-5} sec.

199

4. $v = (1 - 4.5 \times 10^{-18})\,c$; $d = 3 \times 10^{-13}$ cm.

CHAPTER VI

1. -10^{-7} seconds, $.5 \times 10^{-14}$ seconds

2. no

4. a. 600/c sec.

    b. 1333/c sec.

    c. 1667/c sec.

    d. 1067/c sec.

6. 166.67 meters

The slices aren't simultaneous in the stick's frame of reference.

CHAPTER VII

1. $20/\sqrt{3}$ seconds

2. a. x = 4/5 meters

    b. $-3/5\,c$ seconds. ($c = 3 \times 10^8$ m/sec.)

3. a. $\dfrac{15}{17}\,c$

    b. 80, 100, 80 meters.

    c. $\dfrac{234}{c}, \dfrac{167}{c}, \dfrac{133}{c}$ seconds

4. a. $v = \dfrac{1}{2}\sqrt{c^2 + 3\,v_\pi^{\,2}}$

    b. $\theta = \tan^{-1}\dfrac{c}{\sqrt{3}\,v_\pi}$

5. a. c.

    b. $\dfrac{\frac{4}{5}c - v_\mu}{1 + \frac{4\,v_\mu}{5\,c}}$

CHAPTER VIII

1. $v = 10^{-3} c/\sqrt{3}$

2. $p_\gamma c^2 / \sqrt{p_\gamma^{\,2} c^2 + M^2 c^4}$

3. $M = 9/16$ m

4. P (galaxy) = $3.5 \times 10^{49} \frac{\text{kgm-m}}{\text{sec}}$ $v_{\text{proton}} = (1\text{-}1.04 \times 10^{-136})$ c

CHAPTER IX

1. K.E. = 29.064 Bev
   p = 29.986 Mev/c
   v = .9995 c

2. 1.2 Mev

3. 8.1×10^{23} joules
   $K.E./Mc^2 = 9$

4. no

5. a. 234.0437 amu
   c. no

CHAPTER X

2. p = .478 Mev/c $\nu = 1.16 \times 10^{20}$ sec^{-1}.

3. 2.4×10^{-10} cm.

4. no

CHAPTER XI

1. a. 332 Mev
   b. 192 Mev
   c. 301 Mev/c
   d. .91 c

2. 1.63×10^{22} sec^{-1}.

3. .49 Mev/c

4. .166 cm/sec

5. .024 Å,   .087 e.v.

7. $7\, m_p\, c^2$

8. K at rest if $E_\gamma = \dfrac{\left(M_\Lambda^{\,2} - (M_p - M_K)^2 \right) c^2}{2(M_p - M_K)}$

CHAPTER XII

1. our frame: $p = .383$ Mev/c, $E = .639$ Mev.
    other frame: $p = -.213$ Mev/c $E = .555$ Mev.

2. center of mass frame: $E_\pi = 173$ Mev $\quad p_\pi = 102$ Mev/c
    laboratory frame: $\quad\quad E_\pi = 425$ Mev $\quad p_\pi = 400$ Mev/c

3. $\Delta \nu / \nu = 10^{-3}$

4. .07 $\overset{o}{A}$, no.

CHAPTER XIV

1. a. .94c

2. a. 10^6 Newtons.
    b. 3.7×10^{22} Joules.
    c. 2.1×10^{14} Joules/second.

3. 0.2 radians.

TABLE OF SELECTED PHYSICAL CONSTANTS

Speed of light	c	3.00×10^{8} meters/sec
Gravitational constant	G	6.67×10^{-11} nt-m^2/kgm^2
Planck's constant	h	6.63×10^{-34} joule-sec
Boltzmann's constant	k	1.38×10^{-23} joule/^{o}K
Electron charge	e	1.60×10^{-19} coulombs
Electron mass	m_e	9.11×10^{-31} kgm
Electron mass-energy	$m_e c^2$	.511 Mev
Permittivity constant	ϵ_o	8.85×10^{-12} farad/meter
Permeability constant	μ_o	1.26×10^{-6} henry/meter

TABLE OF SELECTED CONVERSION FACTORS

1 radian = 57.3 degrees

1 mile = 1.61 kilometers

1 Ångstrom unit = 10^{-10} meters

1 light-year = 9.48×10^{15} meters

1 year = 3.16×10^{7} seconds

1 electron volt = 1.60×10^{-19} joules

1 atomic mass unit (amu) = 1.66×10^{-27} kgm

1 kilogram of mass x c^2 = 9.0×10^{16} joules of mass-energy

INDEX

205